Practice

Maths and English

BUMPER BOOK

**Age 5–7
Years 1–2**
Key Stage 1

Acknowledgment

The Publishers would like to thank the following for permission to reproduce copyright material:

p.60 'On the Ning Nang Nong' from Silly Verse for Kids by Spike Milligan. Puffin Books, 1989.

Every effort has been made to trace all copyright holders, but if any have been inadvertently overlooked the Publishers will be pleased to make the necessary arrangements at the first opportunity.

Hachette UK's policy is to use papers that are natural, renewable and recyclable products and made from wood grown in sustainable forests. The logging and manufacturing processes are expected to conform to the environmental regulations of the country of origin.

Orders: please contact Bookpoint Ltd, 130 Milton Park, Abingdon, Oxon OX14 4SB. Telephone: (44) 01235 827720. Fax: (44) 01235 400454. Lines are open 9.00a.m.–5.00p.m., Monday to Saturday, with a 24-hour message answering service. Visit our website at www.hoddereducation.co.uk.

© Louis Fidge, Richard Cooper, Paul Broadbent 2013
Teacher's tips © Najoud Ensaff, Paul Broadbent and Matt Koster 2013
First published in 2013 exclusively for WHSmith by
Hodder Education
An Hachette UK Company
338 Euston Road
London NW1 3BH

Impression number   10 9 8 7 6 5 4 3 2 1
Year   2018 2017 2016 2015 2014 2013

Cover illustration by Oxford Designers and Illustrators Ltd
Character illustrations: Beehive Illustration
All other illustrations Fakenham Prepress Solutions, Fakenham, Norfolk NR21 8NN
Typeset in Folio by Fakenham Prepress Solutions, Fakenham, Norfolk NR21 8NN
Printed in Italy

A catalogue record for this title is available from the British Library.

ISBN: 978 1444 188 073

Advice for parents

Maths and English *Practice* bumper book

The books in the *Practice* series are designed to practise and consolidate children's work in school. They are intended for children to complete on their own, but you may like to work with them for the first few pages.

This bumper book provides a selection of titles from the *Practice* range for children aged 5–7. This selection consists of three English titles: *English Practice*, *Writing and Punctuation Practice* and *Grammar and Punctuation Practice*; and three Maths titles: *Maths Practice*, *Solving Problems Practice* and *Mental Maths Practice*.

Details for all of the titles in the *Practice* Key Stage 1 series can be found on the inside front cover of this book.

When using this book with your child, the following points will help:

- Don't ask your child to do too much at once. A 'little and often' approach is a good way to start.
- Reward your child with lots of praise and encouragement. These should be enjoyable activities for them.
- Discuss with your child what they have learned and what they can do.
- The '**Get ready**' section provides a gentle warm-up for the topic covered on the page.
- The '**Let's practise**' section is usually the main activity. This section helps to consolidate understanding of the topic.
- The '**Have a go**' section is often a challenge or something interesting that your child can go away and do which is related to the topic. It may require your child to use everyday objects around the home.
- The '**How have I done?**' section at the end of each book is a short informal test that should be attempted when all the units have been completed. It is useful for spotting gaps in knowledge, which can then be revisited at a suitable moment.
- The '**Teacher's tips**' are written by practising classroom teachers. They give useful advice on specific topics or skills, to deepen your child's understanding and confidence and to help you help your child.

Contents

WRITING

GRAMMAR AND PUNCTUATION

MATHS

SOLVING PROBLEMS

MENTAL MATHS

Welcome to Kids Club!

Hi, readers. My name's Charlie and I run Kids Club with my friend Abbie. Kids Club is an after-school club that is very similar to one somewhere near you.

We'd love you to come and join our club and see what we get up to!

I'm Abbie and I run Kids Club with Charlie. Let's meet the children who will work with you on the activities in this book.

My name is Jamelia. I look forward to Kids Club every day. There is always fun to be had with the activities we do. The sports and games are my favourites.

Hi, I'm Megan. I've made friends with all the children at Kids Club. I like the outings and trips we go on the best.

Hello, my name's Kim. Kids Club is a great place to chill out after school. My best friend is Alfie. He's a bit naughty but he means well!

I'm Amina. I like to do my homework at Kids Club. Charlie and Abbie are always very helpful. We're like one big happy family.

Greetings, readers. My name's Alfie! Everybody knows me here. Come and join our club. We'll have a wicked time together!

Now you've met us all, tell us something about yourself. All the children filled in a '**Personal Profile**' when they joined. There's one on the next page for you to complete.

Personal Profile

INSERT PHOTO OF YOURSELF HERE

Name: _____

Age: _____

School: _____

Home town: _____

Pets: _____

My favourite:

- book is _____,

- film is _____,

- food is _____,

- sport is _____.

My hero is _____ because _____
_____.

When I grow up, I want to be a _____.

If I could be king or queen for the day, the first thing I would do is _____

_____.

If I could be any animal for a day, I would be a _____

_____.

Practice

English

Core English skills for Year 1

1: The alphabet

Look at our alphabet wall.
There are 26 letters of the alphabet.
There are 21 **consonants**, in **black**.
There are five **vowels**, in **red**.
All words are made up of letters.
Each word must have at least one vowel sound in it.

 **Get ready**

Fill in the missing letters.

1

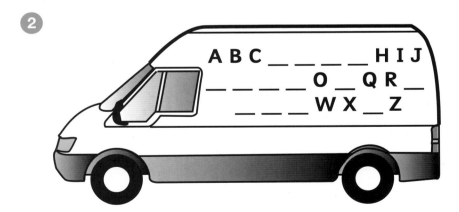

a b c d e __ g h __ j
k __ __ __ o __ __ r s
__ u v __ __ __ z

2

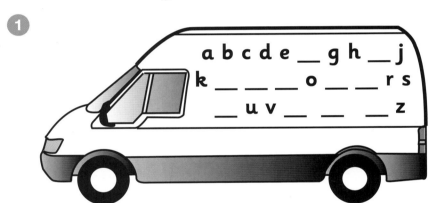

A B C __ __ __ __ H I J
__ __ __ __ __ O __ Q R __
__ __ __ W X __ Z

Teacher's tips

Remembering the order of the alphabet can be difficult. Why don't you look on the internet for an alphabet song to help you? Don't get confused – remember letters on a computer keyboard are not in alphabetical order!

Which letter comes **after** each of these?

3 d ___   4 g ___   5 k ___

6 n ___   7 q ___   8 t ___

Which letter comes **between** each of these?

9   b ___ d   10   h ___ j   11   o ___ q

12   s ___ u   13   v ___ x   14   x ___ z

Which letter comes **before** each of these?

15   ___ c   16   ___ f   17   ___ n

18   ___ r   19   ___ t   20   ___ x

Write the name of the letter that sounds like:

21   a busy insect _b_

22   something you swim in ___

23   a small green vegetable ___

24   a long line of people ___

25   a hot drink ___

26   a female sheep ___

27   Colour in the **vowels** on this computer keyboard.

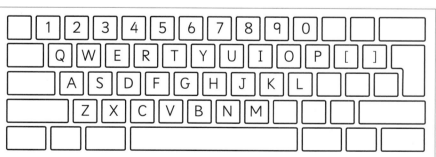

Have a go

Say the names of the letters of the alphabet without looking at them.

2: Word-making

Say the **sound** of each letter aloud and then make the words.

h + e + n   d + o + g   c + a + t

Get ready

Fill in the missing letter at the **beginning** of each word. The first one has been done for you.

1 m   p   **2** b   d   **3** n   l   **4** c   p

_m_ ug   ___ at   ___ og   ___ in

Fill in the missing letter at the **end** of each word.

5 m   n   **6** d   p   **7** g   t   **8** f   g

su ___   mo ___   ha___   fa ___

Let's practise

Say the sound of each letter aloud and then make the words.

9   **10**   **11**   **12**   **13**

p + a + n   l + e + g   p + o + t   b + e + d   b + u + n

<u>pan</u>   _____   _____   _____   _____

Fill in the missing vowels.
Write the words that **rhyme**.

14    a c _a_ t on a m _a_ t   ___cat___   ___mat___

15   a t ___ d on a b ___ d   _____ _____

16   a k ___ ng with a r ___ ng   _____ _____

17   a cl ___ ck on a r ___ ck   _____ _____

18   a m ___ g and a j ___ g   _____ _____

Have a go

All words must contain at least one vowel sound. Choose and write down any ten words from a reading book. Underline the vowels in the words. Which word contains the most vowels?

Teacher's tips

Words that rhyme have the same end sounds, so in the phrase **the man with a pan** the two words that rhyme are **man** and **pan** because they both have an **-an** sound at the end of them.

3: Writing sentences (1)

Words in a **sentence** are written **in order**.

This helps **sentences to make sense**.

can run I ☒   I can run. ☑

Write these words in order. Make some sensible sentences.

1 can hop. I   <u>I can hop</u>.

2 cow A moos.   _____

3 Fish swim. can   _____

4 is cold. Ice cream   _____

5 sun The yellow. is   _____

6 sing. I can   _____

7 sky The blue. is _____

8 eggs. Hens lay   _____

9 cat milk. A likes   _____

10 can a bike. ride I   _____

Teacher's tips

In the **Get ready** section, knowing that sentences start with capital letters and end in full stops will help you to spot the first and last words in each sentence!

Let's practise

Choose the best word to **complete** each sentence.

drum   bike   sea   cake   dog

frog   snake   grass   bird   book

11   The _____ is green.

12   A _____ barks

13   I can read a _____.

14   You bang a _____.

15   You swim in the _____.

16   A _____ sings.

17   A _____ hops.

18   You eat a _____.

19   A _____ hisses.

20   A _____ has got two wheels.

Have a go

Make up some sentences containing these words:

car	bike	train	ship	rocket	submarine
	helicopter	scooter	fire engine	tractor	

4: Capital letters and full stops

A sentence begins with a **capital letter**.
Many sentences end with a **full stop**.

This is a clock**.**

Get ready

Circle the **capital letter** at the **beginning** of each sentence.
Circle the **full stop** at the **end** of each sentence.

1 Here is a monkey.   **2** This is an apple.

3 I can see a goat.   **4** Here is a car.

5 This is a dog.   **6** I can see a cat.

Teacher's tips

If you get stuck on the **Have a go** section, make a list of five words that describe your school. Then put each of these words into a sentence.

Copy these sentences.
Begin each sentence with a **capital letter**.
End each sentence with a **full stop**.

7   a frog can hop

8   a fish can swim

_____

9   a kangaroo can jump

10   a lion can run

_____

11   a bird can fly

12   an ant can crawl

_____

13   a monkey has got long arms

14   an elephant has got a trunk

_____

Have a go

Write five sentences about your school.

5: The *ch*, *sh* and *th* sounds

Sometimes two consonants **blend** together and make **one sound**.
Read these words aloud and listen to the sounds *ch*, *sh* and *th* in them.

cheese

sheep

mo**th**

Get ready

Complete the words. Write the words.

1 **ch** c̲h̲at   _____eck   _____ip   _____op

     c̲h̲at   _____   _____   _____

2 **sh** _____ed   _____op   _____ip   _____ut

     _____   _____   _____   _____

3 **th** _____in   _____ick   _____ink   _____ump

     _____   _____   _____   _____

Now read all the words you made.

Teacher's tips

If you find it hard to think of words beginning with these phonemes, here is a clue to get you started: **sh...** a large boat on water.

Let's practise

Choose **ch**, **sh** or **th** to complete each word.
Write the words you make.

4

shop

shop

5

_____ick

_____

6

ba_____

_____

7

tor_____

_____

8

_____op

_____

9

_____ed

_____

10

bru_____

_____

11

pa_____

_____

12

_____ief

_____

13

fi_____

_____

14

_____ips

_____

15

_____rone

_____

16

Write two words that **begin** with:
   ch   **sh**   **th**

_____   _____   _____

_____   _____   _____

17

Write two words that **end** with:
   ch   **sh**   **th**

_____   _____   _____

_____   _____   _____

Have a go

Look through a reading book and write down five **ch** words, five **sh** words and five **th** words from it.

6: Special names

When we write **someone's name**, or the **name of a day**, we should start it with a **capital letter**.

Kim's birthday is **T**uesday.

 **Get ready**

Write each child's name again correctly.

①  charlie

_____

② abbie

_____

③ jamelia

_____

④  megan

_____

⑤  kim

_____

⑥  amina

_____

⑦  alfie

_____

Teacher's tips

Here's a rhyme to help you remember how to spell the names of days:
It's **o** in M**o**nday, but **u** in S**u**nday!
A **u** in Th**u**rsday and Sat**u**rday too.
A tricky **e** in Tu**e**sday, a silent **d** in We**d**nesday
But the **i** in Fr**i**day is easy for you.

Write the days of the week in **order**.

Friday   Monday   Saturday   Sunday

Thursday   Wednesday   Tuesday

8 Sunday   M_____   _____   _____

_____   _____   _____

Fill in the **name** of each **day** in this rhyme.

9

Solomon Grundy

Born on M_____ .

Christened on T_____ .

Married on _____ .

Ill on _____ .

Worse on _____ .

Died on _____ .

Buried on _____ .

That was the end of Solomon Grundy.

Have a go

Look at a calendar and write down the names of the months in order. Remember to begin each month with a capital letter.

7: Groups of words

We sometimes **group** words together. These words are all the names of **animals**.

elephant

giraffe

lion

Get ready

Complete the name of each animal and write the whole name below.

1

d _u_ ck

duck

2

b___t

_____

3

d___g

_____

4

c___t

_____

5

f___x

_____

6

___orse

_____

7

h___n

_____

8

___ow

_____

9

___ird

_____

10

r___t

_____

Let's practise

Sort the following **fruit** and **vegetables** into two groups of words.

banana   onion   peas   orange

broccoli   pear   carrot   strawberries

cherries   potato   cabbage   grapes

fruit	vegetables

Have a go

Fold a page in half. On one half write down the name of five different flowers. On the other half, write down the name of five different trees.

Teacher's tips

If you're not sure whether an item is a fruit or vegetable, you can always look up the word in a dictionary to help. If you can't think of any flowers or trees, perhaps an adult can help you.

8: The *ee* and *oo* sounds

Sometimes two vowels **blend** together and make **one sound**.
Read these words aloud and listen to the sounds *ee* and *oo* in them.

tr**ee**

m**oo**n

Get ready

Make these words.

1

sh + ee + p

sheep

f + ee + t

_____

th + r + ee

_____

s + w + ee + t

_____

2

h + oo + p

_____

b + oo + t

_____

s + t + oo + l

_____

s + p + oo + n

_____

Now read all the words you made.

Let's practise

Underline the **ee** and **oo** words in these sentences.

3

You sweep with a broom.

4

Look at the green apples in the tree.

5

I sat on a stool by the pool.

6

When the moon is out I go to sleep.

7

Can you see three bees?

8

I put my boot on my foot.

Make a list of the **ee** and **oo** words.

9 *ee* words

10 *oo* words

Have a go

Try changing the **ee** to **oo** in the words in this unit. Can you make any sensible words? e.g. **sweep** becomes **swoop**. Now try changing the **oo** to **ee** in the words in this unit. Can you make any sensible words? e.g. **stool** becomes **steel**.

A **sentence** should **make sense**.

A bird can fly. ✓

An elephant can fly. ✗

Get ready

Choose the **correct** word to complete each sentence.

1 You _____ (drink / bang) a drum.

2 You _____ (eat / kick) a cake.

3 You _____ (read / draw) a book.

4 You _____ (climb / run) a ladder.

5 You _____ (swim / ride) a bike.

6 You _____ (sleep / walk) in bed.

Teacher's tips

Sometimes saying a sentence out loud helps you to know whether it makes sense and is right. Try this when you complete the activities on these pages.

Let's practise

Write each sentence again, so it **makes sense**.
The first one has been done for you.

7   I smell with my ears.   <u>I smell with my nose</u>.

8   I hear with my nose.   _____

9   I see with my mouth.   _____

10   I talk with my eyes.   _____

11   I feel with my feet.   _____

12   I walk on my hands.   _____

Complete each sentence correctly.

    bird   clock   chair   pencil   cow   spider

13   You write with me. I am a _____ .

14   I have got four legs. You sit on me. I am a _____ .

15   I eat grass. I give you milk. I am a _____ .

16   I have got wings. I can fly. I am a _____ .

17   I have got two hands and a face. I am a _____ .

18   I have eight legs. I make a web. I am a _____ .

Have a go

Two words in each of these sentences are in the wrong place.
Write the sentences correctly.

We get cows from milk.

The ball kicked the boy.

The web made a spider.

10: Magic 'e'

Read the sentence.

I hate my hat!

What happens when we add the **magic 'e'**?

hat – hat**e**

Get ready

Read each word. Add the magic 'e' and read it again.

①	kit	<u>kite</u>		②	mat	_____
③	rip	_____		④	cap	_____
⑤	hat	_____		⑥	gap	_____
⑦	rob	_____		⑧	cut	_____
⑨	not	_____		⑩	tub	_____
⑪	pin	_____		⑫	mad	_____

Teacher's tips

Did you notice how when you put the magic 'e' on words, the vowels in the new words sound like the name of the vowel letter? The 'a' sound in **hate** sounds like the letter 'a'.

Let's practise

Write the correct word under each picture.

13 tap / tape

tap

14 slid / slide

_____

15 mop / mope

_____

16 mat / mate

_____

17 pip / pipe

_____

18 cub / cube

_____

19 pin / pine

_____

20 tub / tube

_____

21 hat / hate

_____

22 shin / shine

_____

23 rat / rate

_____

24 can / cane

_____

Have a go

One word in each of these sentences has the magic '**e**' missing.
Underline the words with the missing magic '**e**'.

I hop it is a good day tomorrow.
Will the sun shin?
I hat the rain!

When we read a story, we must be able to read the words and **understand what they mean**.

 Get ready

Read this story.

Ben and Mia are on holiday today.
They are going to the seaside. It's not far away.
Ben takes his sunglasses and his hat.
Mia takes her flip-flops and a mat.
Ben has an ice cream. Mia has a lolly to lick.
They have a beach ball to throw and kick.
Ben and Mia paddle in the sea. They laugh and shout.
Max the dog comes in and splashes about.
The sun goes down. It goes all red.
They go back home. It's time for bed.

Teacher's tips

For **Have a go**, perhaps you could go to the library to look for a book by your favourite author. Another idea is to go online to the website of a bookshop and do a search for your favourite author.

 **Let's practise**

Answer these questions.

1. Who is on holiday? _____

2. What is the boy's name? _____

3. What is the girl's name? _____

4. What is the name of the dog? _____

5. Where do they go? _____

6. Is the seaside a long way away? _____

7. What does Ben take? _____

8. What does Mia take? _____

9. What does Ben have to eat? _____

10. What does Mia lick? _____

11. What do they do with the beach ball? _____

12. What do they do when they paddle in the sea? _____

13. Who comes in the water as well? _____

14. What colour does the sun go, when it goes down? _____

15. When they go home, what do Ben and Mia do? _____

Have a go

What is your favourite storybook? Explain why you like it to someone. Find out who the author is (the name of the person who wrote it). Can you find any other books by the same author?

12: Non-fiction

We can learn about different things in **non-fiction** books. They are full of **facts**.

 **Get ready**

Read these facts about foxes.

A fox looks a bit like a dog.
Foxes are brown.
They have a bushy tail. It is called a brush!
Foxes can grow up to 125 centimetres long.
Foxes often live in woods.
In the daytime, foxes stay in their homes called dens.
Some foxes live in towns.
Foxes come out at night to hunt for food.
They often catch small animals to eat.
The female fox is called a vixen
Baby foxes are called cubs.

Teacher's tips

Read the information about foxes line by line once. Then when you answer the questions on page 37, look back at each line in turn. You will find that the answers to each question appear in the order of the lines.

Answer these questions.

1. Do foxes look like dogs or cats?

   _____

2. Are foxes brown or green?

   _____

3. What sort of tail do foxes have?

   _____

4. What is another name for a fox's tail?

   _____

5. How long can foxes grow up to?

   _____

6. Do foxes live in the sea or in woods?

   _____

7. What are the homes of foxes called?

   _____

8. Do some foxes live in towns? _____

9. Do foxes come out in the day or at night to hunt for food?

   _____

10. What do foxes eat? _____

11. What is a female fox called? _____

12. What are baby foxes called? _____

Have a go

Look for some more information on foxes. Look in books in your school or your library. Perhaps you can use a computer to find some information.

How have I done?

Answer these questions to see how well you have done at Kids Club.

If the question is in two or more parts, you must get all the parts right to get a mark.

1 Name the five vowels.

_____ _____ _____ _____ _____

2 Fill in the missing vowels in these words.

p ___ t   b ___ n   b___ d   p ___ n   r ___ t

3 Rearrange these words into a sentence.

barks. dog A   _____

4 Write this sentence again. Punctuate it correctly.

a tiger has got stripes   _____

5 Choose **ch**, **sh** or **th** to complete each word.

ba_____   _____air   _____ed

6 Write this sentence correctly.

alfie got wet on sunday.   _____

7 Underline the odd word out in this group of words.

trousers   coat   kettle   jeans

8 Use **oo** or **ee** to complete each word.

m____n

sh____p

9 Choose the best word to complete the sentence.

baker   doctor   teacher

I help you at school. I teach you to read and write.
I am a _____ .

10 One word in each sentence is spelt incorrectly.
Write each sentence again.

I can ~~rid~~ a bike.   _____

The sun will ~~shin~~ tomorrow.   _____

11 Read the story on page 34 again.

Did Mia and Ben go to the park or to the seaside? _____

12 Read the information on page 36 again.
Is it about lions or
foxes? _____

Well done for working so hard.
We hope you can come back to
Kids Club another time!

Writing

Take the next steps in writing

1: Writing lists

The children are planning a party. They are making lists of all the things they will need.

We use commas to separate things in a list.

hat, cake, balloon, cup

Get ready

Here are the things that the children wrote down. Alfie has mixed them all up! Sort them into lists. There are four words in each list. Remember to put the commas between each word in the lists. The first one has been done for you.

musical chairs   crisps   tag   water
cola   streamers   spoons   fruit   cups   statues   squash
treasure hunt   balloons   lemonade   sandwiches
forks   cakes   plates   party-poppers   flags

1 Amina made a list of drinks

Water, cola, squash, lemonade

2 Megan made a list of decorations.

_____

3 Kim made a list of party games.

_____

4 Jamelia made a list of food.

_____

5 Alfie made a list of things to eat and drink with.

_____

Let's practise

We do not need a comma before the word 'and' when we use it in a list.

**At the party I ate a cake, a sausage,
a sandwich and an apple.**

Add the commas to these sentences.

6 Amina went to the party with Alfie Kim Jamelia and Megan.

7 Alfie danced to pop rap rock and hip-hop music.

8 Kim made lots of decorations such as banners streamers flags and posters.

9 Megan had to move lots of furniture like the chairs tables desks and bookcases.

10 To clean up afterwards Jamelia used brooms cloths dustpans and brushes.

Have a go

Name five friends you would like to invite to a party. Remember to add the commas!

Write lists of your favourite foods, books, animals, games and toys. Use commas in each list.

Teacher's tips

Tick the words in **Get ready** as you go along, so that you don't get confused. For example, look for all the words that are decorations and tick them off as you write them in answer to question 2. Then do the same for questions 3, 4 and 5.

Megan has a penfriend in France. She wants to write and tell her all about the party. See if you can help her.

Here is the letter Megan has written. Help her by adding in the missing words from the list below. If you want to, you can think of others that may fit.

pony   enormous   excited   loudly   arrived   fell   wonderful   gave

Dear Michelle,

On Friday afternoon after school we had a party. We were so _____, everyone was happy. When we _____ we had a drink and something to eat. Alfie was dancing for most of the time. He _____ over, bumped his head and began to cry _____! Just then a clown came over. He gave Alfie an _____ balloon. He stopped crying and we all laughed and cheered. Then a _____ thing happened. The clown _____ each of us a balloon! Mine was in the shape of a beautiful _____. I knew you would have liked one the same.

Write soon!

Megan

Let's practise

So, a recount is retelling something that has happened.

Here is a good way to write a recount.
1. Think about what you want to say.
2. Think about who it happened to, where, when, why and how.
3. Remember the order of events. Use words such as **first**, **then**, **next**, **later**, **after** and **before**.
4. Say why you think things happened.
5. Finish by saying what you thought of the event.

Write a recount in your Kids Club notebook. You could write it about something that has happened to you in real life or choose one of these titles:
- The Day At The Beach
- When I Got Lost
- The Time My Sister Swallowed A Fly!

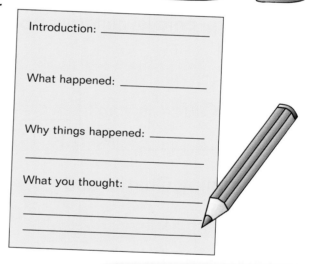

Introduction: _____

What happened: _____

Why things happened: _____
_____

What you thought: _____
_____
_____
_____

Have a go

Everyone likes to receive a postcard. Write one to a friend or relative. Tell them about something that has happened to you recently. Ask them to write back!

Wish you were here

Teacher's tips

A wonderful dessert like ***BAT FLAN*** could help you remember those key words in the *Let's practise* section: **b**efore, **a**fter, **t**hen, **f**irst, **l**ater, **a**fterwards and **n**ext.

3: Writing reports

We have been asked to write a report about Kids Club for the school magazine. It is going to be printed in the next edition! We want you to help us write it.

A report gives information about something or somewhere. It has:

- a title
- an introduction
- information about the subject
- an ending to round off the piece of writing.

Fill in the missing words from the list below.

events help enjoys children Abbie drinks games exciting homework

Kids Club

Kids Club is an _____ after-school club for _____ aged 5 to 11.

It is run by Charlie and _____, who are always ready to _____ and are great fun to have around.

There are lots of things to do and _____ to play. You can catch up on _____ or try some art activities. There are snacks and _____ to keep everyone refreshed.

Sometimes Kids Club organises _____ for the school like a disco or summer fete.

Everyone _____ themselves while they are there. Come and join us!

Let's practise

The children have suggested some other subjects for you to write a report about. Choose one and write a report in your Kids Club notebook.

Title:
Introduction:
_____
_____

Information about
_____
_____
_____
_____
_____

Ending:
_____
_____
_____

- Write about your favourite toy. Write about all its features and what it can do.

- Write a report about keeping pets. What do you need to know if you keep one?

- Write about dangerous animals. Which ones are dangerous to humans and why?

- Write a report about a holiday destination. Where is it and what can you do there?

- Write a report about a football team. What do you know about it? What can you find out to add to your report? Research the football team on the Internet or at the library.

Have a go

Choose a topic you are really interested in. Find out as much about it as you can. Use the Internet, books and a grown-up to help you. Write a report about your topic and draw some pictures. Imagine the reader knows nothing about your subject!

Teacher's tips

Look at the report in **Get ready**. The first sentence is an *Introduction*. The other sentences are all *Information about* Kids Club and the last sentence is the *Ending*. Use this to help you when you write your own reports.

4: Writing instructions

The children are writing some instructions on how to look after the Kids Club hamster. One of them will take the hamster home to look after him during the holidays.

These are instructions on how to feed Hammy the hamster.

The children have used numbers to show the order.

1. Empty old food from the dish.
2. Put fresh hamster food in the dish.
3. Hide treats around the cage for Hammy to find.
4. Make sure the water bottle is full.
5. Give Hammy fresh fruit once a week.

Using labels and drawings helps to make the instructions clearer.

You can check your instructions are in the right order by trying them out yourself.

Get ready

Write five instructions on how to feed a pet cat.

1. _____

2. _____

3. _____

4. _____

5. _____

Let's practise

Megan is going to look after Hammy. Can you help her with some instructions so that she will know what she needs to do every day?

How To Look After A Hamster

You will need:

A cage	A clean cloth
Sawdust	A bowl
Shredded paper for bedding	An exercise ball
Food and water	A rubbish bag

---

1 First, draw one of the items Megan will need in the box above.

2 Now put the following instructions in the right order by putting numbers in the boxes. Look at the clues. Words like **First**, **Secondly** and **Finally** should help you.

☐ Place a handful of shredded paper bedding on top of the sawdust.
☐ Replace the lid of the cage.
☐ Next, empty the old bedding and sawdust into a rubbish bag.
1 First, put Hammy carefully into the exercise ball.
☐ Finally, feed Hammy some fresh food and replace the water bottle.
☐ Wipe all the surfaces clean with a damp cloth.
☐ Cover the bottom of the cage with fresh sawdust.
☐ Put Hammy back in the cage.
☐ Secondly, lift the lid off the cage.

Have a go

Imagine you had a pet robot! Write some instructions for the robot to get from your bedroom to the school gate. Would it walk? Would it catch the bus? Would it need to take anything?

Teacher's tips

Think carefully about what you do before you leave your home in the morning. Make a list. Then think about how you get to school. Make another list of things that you do. This should help you answer **Have a go**.

5: Writing a book review

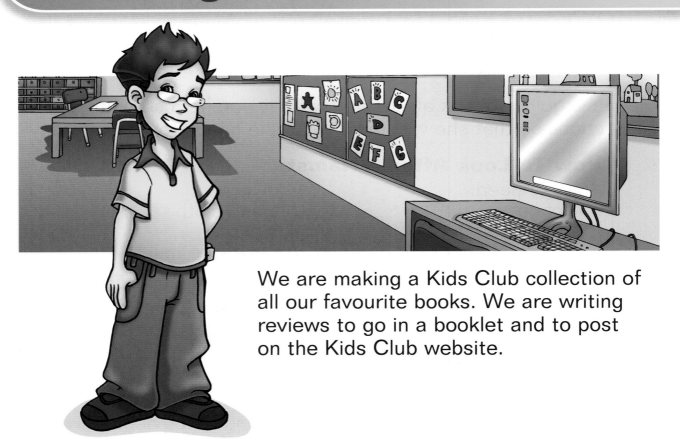

We are making a Kids Club collection of all our favourite books. We are writing reviews to go in a booklet and to post on the Kids Club website.

Get ready

The children have some tips on how to write a good review.

- Plan your writing. How will you start?

- Start a new paragraph for each section. Remember to finish one part before moving on to another.

- **Why?** is a very important word! Tell the reader *why* you like something or *why* you don't.

- Use good words or *vocabulary*. These words will help you: **characters**, **illustrations**, **author**, **beginning** and **ending**.

- Give your *opinion*. Tell the reader what you think and why.

- Use adjectives, or describing words, to make your writing more interesting.

Let's practise

Think about your favourite book or a book you have read recently.

Get a copy of the book.

In your Kids Club notebook, write a review of your book. Use this writing frame to help you.

1. How will you start? What about, '**If you like magical adventures then you will love this book**.'

2. Describe three characters or events in the book. Use good adjectives like **cunning**, **honest**, **wicked**, **cowardly**.

3. Why did you like/dislike the book? Try words like **because**, **exciting**, **funny**, **interesting**, **dull**, **scary**.

4. What about the illustrations? You can use words like **bright**, **cartoon**, **detailed**, **realistic**.

5. Would you want someone else to read this book? Say **why** they should or shouldn't read it.

Title: _____
Author: _____

1. Introduction to the book
_____
_____

2. Describe three characters or events in the book _____
_____
_____

3. Why I like/dislike the book
_____
_____

4. Write about the illustrations in the book _____
_____
_____

5. Why someone else should/shouldn't read it
_____
_____
_____

Have a go

Ask an adult to show you some reviews in newspapers and magazines. Some reviewers give 'stars' or marks out of ten. What sort of marks would you give your favourite book?

Teacher's tips

If you get a bit stuck writing your review try using some of these sentences:
.... is a book about ....
My favourite character is .... because ....
A really .... thing that happens is ....
I really liked it when ....

6: Alphabetical texts

We want to write a glossary of all the things we do at Kids Club. It is going to be displayed on the Kids Club website so everyone can see all the great activities we do.

Get ready

A glossary is a list of words. It should do the following:

- be organised in alphabetical order
- give useful information that is also interesting
- include a brief description of each word so that someone who doesn't know what it means can understand. If you are not sure yourself, write what you think the word means or ask a grown-up.

Let's practise

This is what Charlie and Abbie wrote about Kids Club.

Kids Club is a <u>popular</u> after-school club for pupils aged 5 to 11. It is run by two leaders named Charlie and Abbie, who look after all the children and run all the <u>activities</u>.

The children have a chance to do their homework, catch up on school work or chill out and <u>relax</u> after a busy day.

 There is also the chance to do lots of activities. Some of the <u>favourites</u> include arts and crafts, games in the <u>gym</u>, outings to local attractions and story time.

The children are given <u>healthy</u> snacks and drinks for which there is a small <u>charge</u>. The children have become a great team and most people make friends very quickly.

If you like having fun and want to be part of something <u>special</u>, then sign up for Kids Club now – places go fast!

Now use this guide to write your own glossary in your Kids Club notebook. Include all the words that are underlined in the text that Charlie and Abbie wrote, and write a description or explanation of each word.

Put the words in alphabetical order.

Glossary

Word 1 _____

Word 2 _____

Word 3 _____

Word 4 _____

Word 5 _____

Word 6 _____

Word 7 _____

Word 8 _____

Have a go

Practise using a dictionary. See if you can find the meanings of five words that an adult gives you. Write the meanings in your Kids Club notebook.

Teacher's tips

For **Let's practise**, the first thing you need to do is put the underlined words in alphabetical order. Do this by looking at the first letter of each word. *Activities* will be first. Next, write what the words mean.

7: Writing letters

We want to write a letter to the local council. The playground in the park is broken. Either it needs repairing or a new one needs to be put in. If enough letters are written, then the council might act!

 Get ready

When you write to someone you don't know, you need to write a formal letter.

Formal letters are very polite!

- Plan your writing. What are you going to say?

- Write your address at the top left-hand corner.

- Put today's date underneath the address.

- Start your letter with **Dear Mr**, **Dear Mrs** or **Dear Miss**.

- You cannot write the way you speak. You need to use full words like this: **you are**, **we are**, **would not**, **could not**.

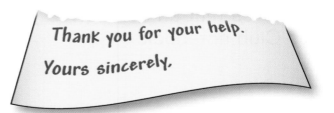

Thank you for your help.
Yours sincerely.

- When you end your letter, use a formal way to finish:
Yours sincerely,
A. Bloggs

Let's practise

Write a letter to Mr Parker from the council. You may wish to use some of these words:

swings   slide   roundabout   dangerous   broken   bench
sincerely   grass   equipment   rubbish   cafe

Write your letter in your Kids Club notebook. Set it out so that it looks like this:

Let's hope we get a new playground soon!

Your address
_____
_____
_____

Date of writing

Dear _____ ,
_____
_____
_____
_____

Yours _____ ,

Your name

Have a go

It's always great to receive a letter. Write a letter to the Prime Minister. Ask about something that you are interested in. See if you get a reply!

Teacher's tips

If you need help with any of the sections on these pages, remember you can always ask a grown-up.

The children are making their own encyclopedia. An encyclopedia is a book that contains lots of information on many subjects and is usually in alphabetical order.

Each of the children has chosen a topic to write about. They want you to write about dinosaurs!

Get ready

You will need to plan your entry.

- Before you start, think about dinosaurs and what information you know about them.

- Now start your entry by introducing the topic. **'Dinosaurs are ...'**

- Write what you know about dinosaurs. *When did they live?* *What did they eat?*

- Think about good vocabulary, for example, **prehistoric**, **fossils**, **meat-eater**, **plant-eater**, **swamp**.

- Use labels and pictures. This will make your information clearer.

Here is a list of words that will help you write your encyclopedia entry.

Tyrannosaurus Rex   Diplodocus   Pteradon   Triceratops
wings   claws   tail   skull   shield   horns   protection
jaws   cutting teeth   chewing teeth   reptiles   armour
scales   fossils   archaeologist   bones   buried   discovered

Let's practise

Write your entry for the encyclopedia in your Kids Club notebook.

Use this guide to help you with your writing.

Remember to include a picture.

Dinosaurs

Introduction:

How do we know about dinosaurs?

What did dinosaurs eat?_____

_____

What did dinosaurs look like?

Draw your favourite dinosaur.

Have a go

Choose your own topic to write about. Read about something you are interested in.

Write an encyclopedia entry about it. Using **How** or **Why** in the title will help. Remember to add illustrations.

Teacher's tips

See if you find an encyclopedia in your school or local library. This will help you to know what to write in your own encyclopedia entries.

9: Planning a story

We are entering a writing competition. We need to write a short story.

We want you to write a story as well. Look at these ideas before you start.

- Think about the setting. *When and where is the story happening?*

- Think about who is in the story. *Are they good or evil; clever or stupid?*

- What sort of story is it? *Is it adventure, mystery, fairy tale, horror or science fiction?*

- Are you in the story: **'I looked around the corner and saw a huge ...'** or are you going to write about somebody else: **'The knight looked around the corner and saw a huge ...'**?

- Make your story exciting! *Choose good vocabulary. Make sure your words fit with the setting and style.*

Here are some examples of titles for different styles of story. Make up some titles of your own for each style.

Adventure story: *Operation X!* _____

Mystery story: *The Secret Statue* _____

Fairy tale: *The Wishing Ring* _____

Horror story: *Night of the Wolf* _____

Science fiction story: *My Sister's An Alien!* _____

Choose one of your answers as the title of the story you are going to plan in the following exercise.

Let's practise

Plan your story in your Kids Club notebook.

Use this guide to help you with
your planning.

- Beginning: Get the reader's attention.
- Middle: Build up the tension. Is there a problem to solve?
- Ending: Tie up the loose ends. Is the ending believable?

Story plan

Title: _____

Beginning:
_____
_____
_____
_____

Middle: _____
_____
_____
_____

Ending: _____
_____
_____
_____

Have a go

When you have planned your story, write it out. Check through
your writing with a grown-up. Can you improve the story? Draw a
picture of the most exciting part.

Teacher's tips

If you get stuck for ideas, think of films you might have seen or books you have read
to help you write some titles for **Get ready** and your own story in **Let's practise**.

10: Writing poems

I love writing poems, especially poems that make people laugh. At Kids Club, we love hearing nonsense poems. These are poems that are funny and don't make any sense.

Read this poem aloud. It always makes us giggle!

On The Ning Nang Nong
by Spike Milligan

On the Ning Nang Nong
Where the cows go Bong!
And the monkeys all say Boo!
There's a Nong Nang Ning
Where the trees go Ping
And the teapots Jibber Jabber Joo.
On the Nong Ning Nang
All the mice go Clang!
And you just can't catch 'em when they do!
So it's Ning Nang Nong!
Cows go Bong!
Nong Nang Ning!
Trees go Ping!
Nong Ning Nang!
The mice go Clang!
What a noisy place to belong,
Is the Ning Nang Ning Nang Nong!

You are going to write your own version. Before you start, draw circles round pairs of rhyming words. Use different coloured pencils. To start, I've coloured the first **Nong** and **Bong** red.

Let's practise

Remember, your version doesn't have to make sense, but you must get the rhymes in the right place!

On the _____ _____ _____

Where the _____ go _____!

And the _____ all say _____!

There's a _____ _____ _____

Where the _____ go _____

And the _____ _____ _____ _____.

On the _____ _____ _____

All the _____ go _____!

And you just can't catch 'em when they do!

So it's _____ _____ _____!

_____ go _____!

_____ _____ _____!

_____ go _____!

_____ _____ _____!

The _____ go _____!

What a noisy place to belong,

Is the _____ _____ _____ _____ _____!

Have a go

Make a list of nonsense words. Put them into a poem of your own.

Teacher's tips

If you're finding this hard, just replace the first letter of all the nonsense words in Spike Milligan's poem and change the animals. Then use these in your own poem. The first line could be *On the Bing Bang Bong*.

11: Haiku

Haiku is a form of poetry. It was invented by a Japanese man called Basho. He wrote poems about the beauty of nature. Haiku often had 17 syllables, contained a clue to the season and consisted of just three lines.

Here is a haiku that Basho wrote after visiting the site of a great battle from the past.

All that remains of	(5 syllables)
Those brave warriors' dreamings –	(7 syllables)
These summer grasses.	(5 syllables)

Three lines   Clue to the season

Get ready

Japanese haiku usually have three lines of five, seven and five syllables. You can use fewer syllables for a free form of haiku. You can use similes in a haiku, for example: **'As swift as a striking snake'**. Let's try thinking of some words to use.

Make a list of words about nature (for example, *tree, hill, bird*).

_____

Make a list of the sounds of nature (for example, *flutter, splash, rustle*).

_____

Let's practise

Here is a haiku I wrote. Which season is it about?

_____

The withering of the leaves
Are the feelings of the trees
Drifting away.

Now write some haiku for Alfie and Megan.

Alfie:

_____

_____

_____

Megan:

_____

_____

_____

Have a go

Make your own book of haiku. Divide it into four sections for the four seasons. You don't have to mention the season, just give the reader a clue.

Teacher's tips

Remember syllables as parts of a word that you can tap out, so the word *hello* has two syllables. The word *bye* has one.

This is a story Abbie read to the children at story time. We thought we had heard it before. Can you see why?

Get ready

The Three Bears

Once upon a time there were three Bears – Mr Bear, Mrs Bear and their son Bear Junior. They all lived in a flat in a skyscraper in New York. One morning they decided to go for a jog while their freshly baked muffins cooled down.

Well, the smell of the muffins was too much for the window cleaner. Her name was Miss Goldsmith or 'Goldie' for short. She had been cleaning the windows and had seen the Bear family go out. Mr Bear had foolishly left the front door open, so Goldie popped in and ate all the muffins! After being so greedy she felt very tired, so she went to the bedroom and fell fast asleep on Junior's bed.

Not long after, the Bears returned.

'Did you leave the door wide open again, Mr Bear?' sighed Mrs Bear. (He was always doing this.)

'No dear,' stuttered Mr Bear, trying to sound as if he was telling the truth.

Mrs Bear went to get the muffins. Where had they gone? Mr Bear noticed a pile of crumbs on the floor next to Junior's chair.

'Who's been eating my muffins?' he said, looking angrily at Bear Junior.

'Don't look at me, Dad. I've been with you all the time!' wailed Junior.

'That's right, Junior,' said Mrs Bear. 'You've been jogging with us!'

The three bears started to argue. In fact they made so much noise that Goldie woke up. She carefully picked up her bucket and cloth and tip-toed out of the flat.

The three Bears were none the wiser. Mr Bear had to go all the way down the stairs (because the lift was broken) to buy some muffins. And do you know what? He never left the door open again!

Let's practise

Can you see how this story is similar to the traditional story of the three bears? Abbie changed the ending and some of the events, and, of course, the setting.

Which traditional tale would you like to rewrite?

Plan your story in your Kids Club notebook. Use this guide to help you with your planning.

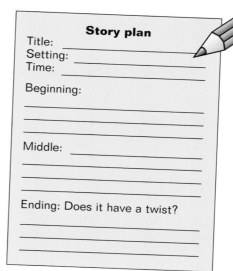

Story plan

Title: _____
Setting: _____
Time: _____

Beginning:
_____
_____

Middle:
_____
_____

Ending: Does it have a twist?
_____
_____

Have a go

Write your story and make it into a book. You could do this on a computer or use paper and card. Illustrate it and read it to a younger child. Do they recognise parts of the story?

Teacher's tips

Perhaps your characters could be on another planet or maybe you could make your story really modern. If you need help, look at a book of fairy tales to remind you of what happens in your chosen tale.

How have I done?

Here are some ideas to get you writing! You will need to write your answers in your Kids Club notebook.

Refer back to the sections in this book to help you.

1 Write a list of presents you would like for your birthday. Don't forget the commas!

2 Write a recount of your most embarrassing moment at school. You can make this up or write about something that really happened!

3 Write a report about your favourite sport or game.

4 Write some instructions for someone on how to look after your pet dragon. Remember, he breathes fire!

5 Write a book review of this book. Has it helped you become a better writer?

6 Play this fun dictionary game with a friend or partner. Choose a random word from a dictionary and get your partner to look it up. Ask them to read out the definition. Do this another three times. Then ask your partner to create a sentence or short paragraph which uses all of the words, *either* in the order they were looked up or in alphabetical order. Now swap over and you have a try.

7 Write a letter to your eldest relative. Tell them what you have been doing at school. You could ask them to write back.

8 Write an article for a magazine. The title is 'Why Did The Dinosaurs Die Out? Research this topic in books and on the internet.

9 Here are five story titles. Choose one, plan your story and then write the story.
- How The Crocodile Got His Smile
- The Mystery Of Bare-Tree Manor
- Mountain Rescue!
- The Vampire's Revenge!
- Escape From Planet Splat!

10 Write a haiku about yourself or a person you know. Try and capture something about their personality. Remember, haiku is a peaceful and thoughtful art!

11 Rewrite the story of Humpty-Dumpty or any other character from a nursery rhyme.

We hope you have enjoyed your time at Kids Club. Write us a letter and let us know how you got on!

Teacher's tips

Gosh, there's lots of writing to do here! Why not choose one or two questions to do at a time. This way, what you write will be as good as possible.

Grammar and Punctuation

Master the core knowledge

1: Simple sentences

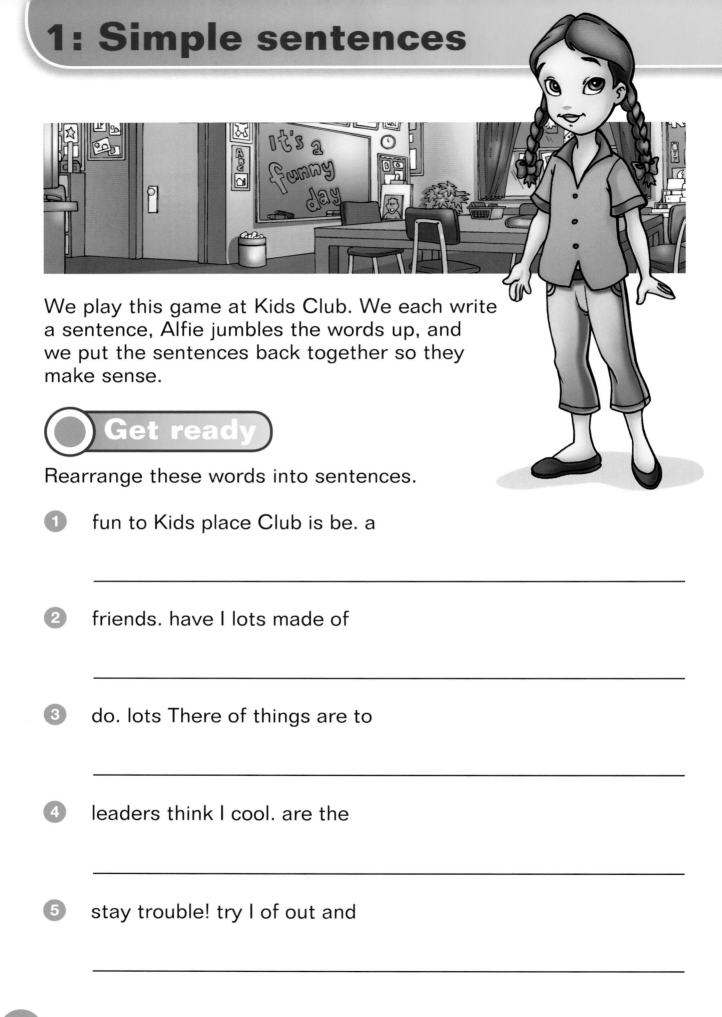

We play this game at Kids Club. We each write a sentence, Alfie jumbles the words up, and we put the sentences back together so they make sense.

Get ready

Rearrange these words into sentences.

1. fun to Kids place Club is be. a

   _____

2. friends. have I lots made of

   _____

3. do. lots There of things are to

   _____

4. leaders think I cool. are the

   _____

5. stay trouble! try I of out and

   _____

Words need to be made into sentences.
Sentences don't make themselves!

Look at these words – **'My rabbit'**
To change that into a sentence I could say, **'I lost my rabbit.'**
Another sentence to follow could be **'I felt sad.'**
Then, **'I found him under my bed!'**

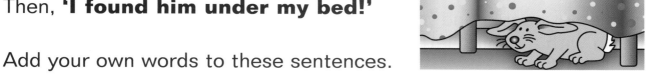

Add your own words to these sentences.

6   I lost my _____. I felt _____. I found it under my
    _____.

7   I like my _____. It is _____. It makes me feel
    _____.

8   I played _____. It is really _____. I enjoy
    _____ as well.

9   I ate a huge _____. It was covered in _____. It
    made me feel _____.

10 I saw a _____. It looked _____. I felt _____.

Write a three-sentence story about going on holiday. Draw a
picture for each of the sentences.

Teacher's tips

Why not write each word from question 1 in **Get ready** on separate post-it notes?
Then move the post-it notes about until you have a sentence that makes sense.
Do the same for questions 2–5.

I have been learning more about sentences. Sentences always begin with a capital letter and usually end with a full stop. When you talk about yourself, always use a capital 'I'.

Names of people and places also begin with a capital letter.

Write these sentences correctly using capital letters and full stops.

1   i like listening to music

_____

2   it makes me feel good

_____

3   i also enjoy playing football

_____

4   it is fun to play with friends

_____

5   i played football on holiday in france

_____

Let's practise

I have written a story but I need your help. There are six sentences in my story.

First read the story aloud and mark where each sentence begins and ends. Then copy the story and add the capital letters and full stops.

we went to the beach it was a sunny day i played in the sand alfie buried my sandals nobody could find them i had to go home barefoot

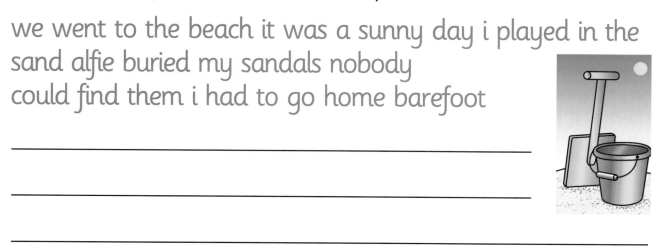

_____

_____

_____

_____

_____

Have a go

Read aloud three pages from a reading book and ignore the full stops. Now read the same three pages aloud again and pause at the full stops.

Which is easier? Which sounds better?

Teacher's tips

Practise your punctuation with Kung Fu! For a capital letter, place your hands in the shape of a triangle over your head. Say 'Capital letter.' For a full stop, throw a short right-handed punch at the air in front of you. Say the word 'Ha!'

3: Using question marks

I like asking lots of questions. My mum says I ask too many! When I write a question I put a question mark at the end of the sentence instead of a full stop.

This is a question mark: **?**

Add a question mark or a full stop to the end of these sentences.

? or **.**

① Would you like to play a game __

② OK, let's play cricket __

③ Alfie has the cricket set __

④ Alfie, can we play with you __

⑤ Of course. Do you have another ball __

Let's practise

Use the words in the box to complete the following sentences.

| Where | Which | What | When | Why | Who | How |

6 _____ is the nearest swimming pool?

7 _____ can we get there?

8 _____ does it open?

9 _____ will be able to take us?

10 _____ don't we go on the bus?

11 _____ is the best slide to go on?

12 _____ shall we do first?

Have a go

Interview a grown-up member of your family.

Write some questions for them to answer. Use the **what**, **where**, **when**, **who** and **why** words.

Ask the grown-up about when they were a child. You could record the conversation.

Teacher's tips

Look at how many questions start with 'Wh' or H'. This will help you to remember question words.

We use exclamation marks when we feel strongly about something, when we are surprised or when giving someone an order. We use exclamation marks instead of full stops, so the next word must start with a capital letter.

Come on, United!

Down, boy!

A new bike, what a wonderful surprise!

 **Get ready**

Add exclamation marks or question marks to these sentences.

? or !

1. Hey, leave my skipping rope alone __

2. Can I borrow it __

3. Hand it back right now __

4. Why can't I play too __

5. Of course you can, but it would be nice if you asked me first __

Let's practise

Copy and punctuate these sentences adding capital letters, full stops, question marks or exclamation marks.

6   which is your favourite ride at the fair

_____

7   i love the dodgems, they're brilliant

_____

8   i always go on the roundabout with alfie

_____

9   we like all of the rides at the fair in freston

_____

10   megan and kim bumped me so hard with their dodgem, i banged my nose on the steering wheel

_____

Have a go

Imagine you saw a Tyrannosaurus Rex looking through your bedroom window!

Write three exclamations you might say.

Teacher's tips

If you enjoyed Kung Fu punctuation, look up some more on *You Tube* under 'Kung Fu punctuation'. You'll be able to see other people doing it and it will help you remember how to punctuate questions and exclamations!

5: Commas in lists

We use commas to separate words in a list.

> **We go to Kids Club on Monday, Tuesday, Wednesday, Thursday and Friday.**

no comma

We don't need a comma before the word 'and' when we use it in a list.

Get ready

Write these sentences adding commas, capital letters and full stops in the correct places.

1 i went to france spain and portugal in a camper van

_____

2 for my birthday i got cards cakes and presents

_____

3 my friend leo can play the piano guitar and violin

_____

4 my best friends are megan amina kim and alfie

_____

5 i love football cricket rugby and swimming

_____

Let's practise

I have set a little quiz for you.

Answer the following questions in sentences, choosing the correct items from each list. Remember to add the commas. I've done the first one for you. Use it to help you answer the rest.

6   Which three are birds?   tiger elephant sparrow eagle hawk

Sparrows, eagles and hawks are birds.

7   Which three are sports?   golf tennis singing hockey reading

_____

8   Which three are drinks?   bread milk squash beef cola

_____

9   Which three are types of food?   book jam mug butter toast

_____

10   Which three are vegetables?   carrots computer sprouts parsnips car

_____

Have a go

My Favourite Three
Write down your favourite three
(a) games   (b) books   (c) types of food

Add the commas to each of your lists.

Teacher's tips

Remember in the **Have a go** section to write in full sentences, and don't forget that sentences start with a capital letter and end in a full stop.

6: Nouns

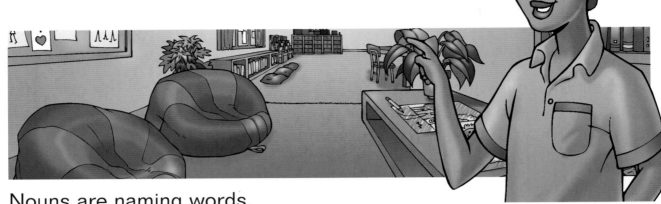

Nouns are naming words.

When we have a noun that begins with a vowel we use **an**.

When the noun begins with a consonant we use **a**.

an elephant	**a** lion
an eagle	**a** giraffe

The vowels are **a e i o u**.

All the other letters are consonants.

Get ready

Put either 'a' or 'an' before these nouns.

1. ____ ruler, ____ pencil, ____ apple

2. ____ hat, ____ shirt, ____ sock

3. ____ egg, ____ orange, ____ onion

4. ____ car, ____ aeroplane, ____ bicycle

5. ____ insect, ____ snake, ____ octopus

A **proper noun** is the name of a person, place or thing. Proper nouns always begin with a capital letter.

> My name is **C**harlie. I help run **K**ids **C**lub.
> It runs from **S**eptember to **J**uly.

Rewrite the sentences, adding capital letters for the proper nouns.

6   We went to london to see the queen at buckingham palace.

_____

7   mr jones was the coach driver.

_____

8   We went on saturday with charlie and abbie.

_____

9   alfie got lost in saint james's park.

_____

10 He was found by mr jones and amina.

_____

Have a go

Make an information sheet about yourself. Write and complete these statements on a piece of paper. Decorate it and put it on your wall.

My name is …
I live in the village/town/city of …
I was born in the month of …
My best friend is …

Teacher's tips

To help you learn to use *an* before a vowel, remember the saying : '*An* apple a day keeps the doctor away.' This might help you.

7: Adjectives

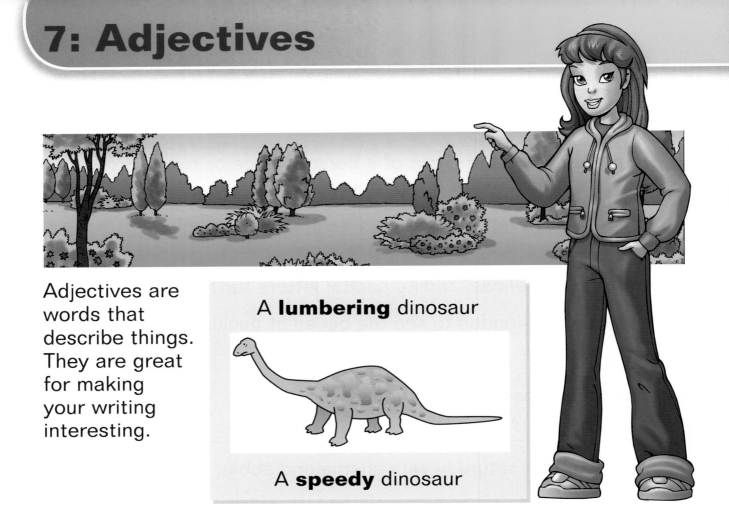

Adjectives are words that describe things. They are great for making your writing interesting.

A **lumbering** dinosaur

A **speedy** dinosaur

Get ready

Choose a different adjective from the box to complete each sentence.

| matted | smelly | terrible | long | hairy |

① My dog Ollie is a very _____ dog.

② When he gets wet he smells _____!

③ He needs to be brushed so his fur doesn't become _____.

④ We love taking Ollie for _____ walks.

⑤ We make sure we pick up any _____ mess that he makes!

Let's practise

Look at this picture. There are five adjectives and five nouns around it. Find examples of these words in the picture and put them in the correct columns in the table.

angry

surprised

stick   pond

smart

drenched   lady

shaggy

mud   clothes

ADJECTIVES	NOUNS

Have a go

Think about your favourite toy or teddy. Write as many adjectives as you can to describe it.

Now think of something you don't like – sprouts or dirty socks, perhaps. Write as many adjectives as you can to describe it.

Use a dictionary or thesaurus to help you.

Teacher's tips

Some of the adjectives in the **Let's practise** section are also verbs. We'll be learning about verbs on the next page!

8: Verbs

A verb is a doing word, like 'run' or 'swim'.

Sentences need a verb so that they make sense.

> This is *not* a sentence: 'a whale in the sea'
> This is a sentence: **A whale swims in the sea**.

Why? Because it has the verb 'swim' and it has a capital letter at the beginning and a full stop at the end.

Get ready

Add a verb from the box to each sentence.

| gobbles   climbs   drops   breaks   travels |

1. The squirrel _____ up the tree.

2. My brother _____ his ice-cream.

3. The car _____ along the road.

4. The tiger _____ up his meal.

5. The stone _____ the window.

Let's practise

A verb is sometimes made up of two words.

> Alfie **is throwing** the ball.
> Kim and Amina **are playing** football.

Add either 'is' or 'are' to these sentences.

6   We _____ going to the beach.

7   The sun _____ shining.

8   Alfie _____ swimming in the sea.

9   Why _____ he waving?

10   _____ you coming in too?

11   The sea _____ looking very warm.

12   Swimming _____ a great idea.

13   We _____ all going to jump in!

14   Who _____ going to be first?

15   Arrgh! The water _____ freezing!

Have a go

Write a list of all the things you do at home during the day. Find all the verbs, the doing words, in your list. For example, I **clean** my teeth.

Teacher's tips

Sometimes reading aloud what you have written helps you to spot mistakes. Try this as you complete the **Let's practise** section.

9: Time connectives

Some words and phrases help connect sentences together. They usually go at the start of or in the middle of sentences.

These words and phrases are useful when you want to write about things that happen over time or in a particular order.

after that	**first**	**next**	**later**	**meanwhile**
then	**after a while**		**finally**	**eventually**
	afterwards	**before**	**secondly**	

These are all time connectives.

Get ready

Choose one of the time connectives from the box above to fill in each gap.

First we will use them at the beginning of a sentence.

How To Make A Jam Sandwich

1 _____, butter two slices of bread.

2 _____, choose your favourite flavour of jam.

3 _____, spread the jam on the slices of bread.

4 _____, place the two slices together to make the sandwich.

5 _____, enjoy eating your sandwich!

Let's practise

Now use the time connectives to link these sentences.

Choose the one which sounds best to fill in each gap.

The first one has been done for you.

6 ___First___ , we went to the shopping centre. ___Afterwards___ we had a meal.

7 I had a salad. _____ , I had some ice cream.

8 When I got home I played with Megan. _____ , we got tired.

9 My mum picked me up. _____ , we got home through the traffic.

10 I stayed awake for ages. _____ , I dropped off to sleep.

Have a go

Write out the story of Cinderella or a story you know very well.

Use as many time connectives in your writing as you can. Think of some more time connectives that you could use.

Teacher's tips

Why not write all those time connectives onto a lovely bit of card so that you can keep it handy for the **Have a go** *section* or any piece of writing, in fact!

The present tense means something that happens now:

'I **sing** a song.'

The past tense means something that has already happened:

'I **sang** a song.'

The future tense means something that will happen:

'I **will sing** a song.'

Circle the word that makes each sentence correct in the present tense.

1 I go / goes to Kids Club.

2 We clean / cleans the art area.

3 You sees / see a film at the cinema.

4 Alfie are / is the star pupil today.

5 But then Alfie breaks / break a vase!

Write a postcard to a friend telling them what you did in the holidays. Write in the past tense.

_____

_____

_____

_____

Now write a postcard describing what you will do on your next holiday. Write in the future tense.

_____

_____

_____

_____

 Have a go

Listen to a sports commentator on the TV or radio. Try and hear when they are speaking in the past, present and future tenses.

He is clean through on goal! (present)

He missed a chance like that last week! (past)

He will play for England next season. (future)

Teacher's tips

Useful starting words for tenses are:
'Today' at the start of your present tense sentence.
'Yesterday' or 'Last week' at the start of your past tense sentence.
'Tomorrow' or 'Next week' at the start of your future tense sentence.

11: Adverbs

Adverbs are great for giving extra meaning to your verbs or sentences.

They describe how, where, by how much, how often, or when something happens.

Abbie sang the song **beautifully**.

'Beautifully' describes *how* Abbie sang.

Amina has a piano lesson **soon**.

'Soon' tells us *when* Amina has a piano lesson.

Charlie flew the kite **outside**.

'Outside' tells us *where* Charlie flew the kite.

Kim **never** eats sprouts.

'Never' tells us *how often* Kim eats sprouts.

Alfie **almost** fell out of the tree.

'Almost' tells us by *how much* something happened.

Get ready

Write a sentence that includes each of these adverbs. The first one has been done for you.

1. silently  The door closed silently.

2. later _____

3. inside _____

4. often _____

5. really _____

Let's practise

Choose an adverb from the box below
and complete the sentences.

noisily   carefully   cleverly   dangerously   there   yesterday

6   The aircraft flew _____ over our heads and made my ears hurt.

7   The car was _____ close to the edge of the cliff.

8   I don't want to go to that shop again. We went there _____ !

9   The girl stepped _____ around the broken glass.

10   'Look, over _____ !' said the Captain.

11   The parrot _____ took the lid off the bottle with his beak.

Have a go

Look at your favourite reading book. Read through and make a note of the '**ly**' adverbs that you find. Can you turn the sentences in the book into funny ones by changing the adverbs? Here is an example:

The dragon roared **fiercely**.
The dragon roared **sweetly**!

Teacher's tips

A lot of adverbs end in *ly* but some do not. To remember the ones mentioned here, memorise these sentences: We *almost never* went to the lake but *yesterday* we went *there*. We were *soon outside*, enjoying ourselves.

How have I done?

Here is a chance to find out how well you have done at Kids Club.

1   Rearrange these words into a sentence.

robots over The city. took the

_____

2   Add a full stop and capital letter to this sentence.

i went to see my friends at the playground

_____

3   Add either a full stop or a question mark to these sentences.

The bus is very full
Do you think we will be able to get on

_____

_____

4   Add a full stop or an exclamation mark to each of these sentences.

A cat makes a good pet

_____

Get out of this room right now

_____

5   Add the commas to this list.

I went to the shops and bought a hat some make-up funny trousers juggling balls and a unicycle.

6 Put either 'a' or 'an' before these nouns.

___ orange, ___ apple, ___ banana, ___ apricot, ___ pineapple

7 Choose an adjective from the box to complete these sentences.

The crocodile has a very _____ skin.

Its teeth are long and _____.

Salt-water crocodiles can grow to _____ sizes.

sharp

huge

scaly

8 Turn these into sentences by adding a verb and the correct punctuation.

a horse in the field _____

the car on the track _____

9 Add a time connective to link these two sentences.

It was raining heavily. _____ it stopped and the sun came out.

10 Write a sentence in the past tense using this verb: swim.

_____

Write a sentence in the present tense using this verb: run.

_____

Write a sentence in the future tense using this verb: jump.

_____

Circle the adverbs in this list.

cow   proudly   table   shout   she   quickly   happily

Thank you for joining us at Kids Club. We hope you have enjoyed your stay. Come back and see us soon!

Teacher's tips

For question 10, remember sometimes verbs in the past tense do not always end in *ed*. For example the verb 'sing' changes to 'sang'.

Maths

Master the core skills

I count how many children come to Kids Club each day. Can you count these numbers with me?

1 one	2 two	3 three	4 four	5 five	6 six	7 seven	8 eight	9 nine	10 ten

Get ready

1 Trace the numbers.
Draw lines to join the numbers to the matching words.

sixteen	fourteen	eighteen	eleven	seventeen

fifteen	twelve	thirteen	twenty	nineteen

Teacher's tips

The teen numbers often cause problems as they sound different from other numbers up to one hundred. ('Twenty-three' might make more sense than thirteen!) Encourage your child to practise saying each number and writing them in figures and words.

| 11 eleven | 12 twelve | 13 thirteen | 14 fourteen | 15 fifteen | 16 sixteen | 17 seventeen | 18 eighteen | 19 nineteen | 20 twenty |

 Let's practise

2 Write each number carefully. Say them aloud as you write them.

11 → eleven   16 → sixteen

12 → twelve   17 → seventeen

13 → thirteen   18 → eighteen

14 → fourteen   19 → nineteen

15 → fifteen   20 → twenty

Have a go

3 Write the number word.

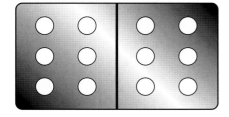      

_____   _____   _____

_____   _____

2: Counting

I like bird watching on Kids Club outings. Can you help me count these birds? Try crossing each bird as you count, it will help you know the ones you have already counted.

Get ready

Count the birds and write the numbers.

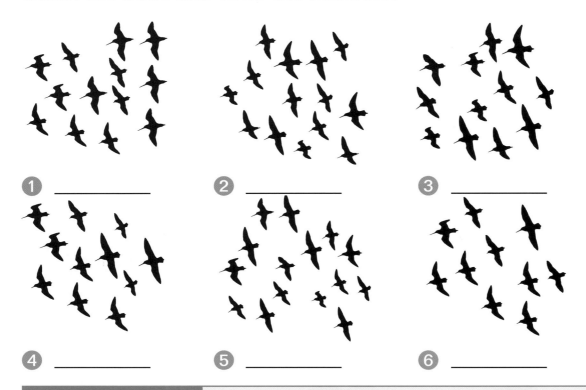

1 _____   2 _____   3 _____

4 _____   5 _____   6 _____

Teacher's tips

Encourage your child to count:

- objects that can be touched or moved, such as toys, coins and fruit
- objects that can be touched but cannot move, such as pictures in books
- objects that cannot be touched or moved, such as objects in the distance
- sounds, such as clapping, banging a drum or clicking fingers.

Let's count.
Count forwards from 1 to 20.
Count backwards from 20 to 1.

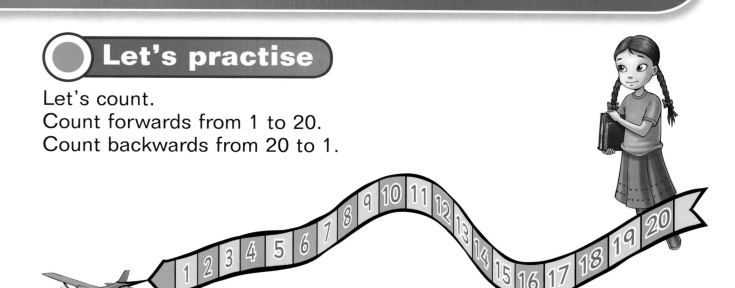

Write the missing numbers.

7 6   7   ☁   9   ☁   ☁   12   13   14

8 9   10   11   ☁   13   ☁   ☁   16   17

9 18   17   16   15   ☁   13   ☁   11   ☁

10 14   ☁   12   11   ☁   ☁   8   7   6

Have a go

There are 6 raindrops.
Draw 10 more raindrops.

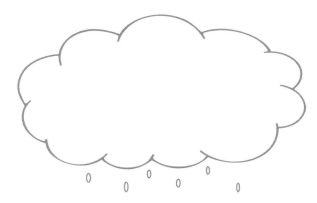

11 There are _____ raindrops altogether.

3: Numbers to 100

We have a garden at Kids Club and I planted flowers in rows of 10. It's easy to count in tens. Say these numbers up to one hundred.

10	20	30	40	50	60	70	80	90	100
ten	twenty	thirty	forty	fifty	sixty	seventy	eighty	ninety	one hundred

● Get ready

1 Join these numbers in order.

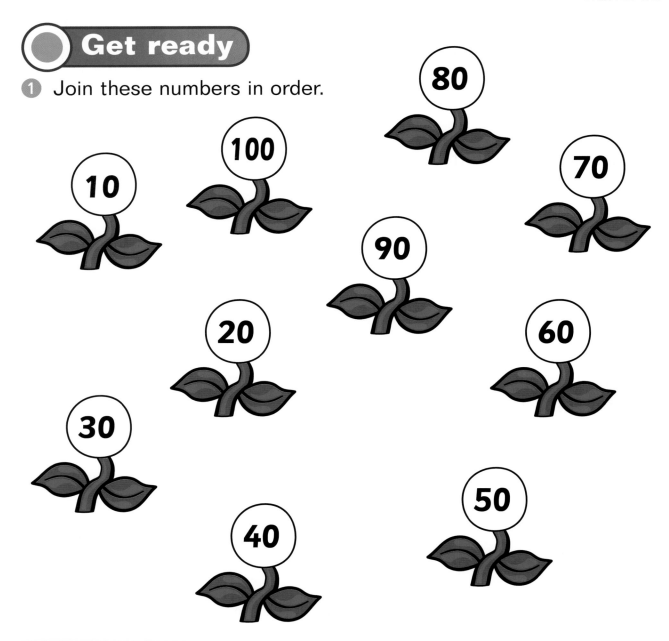

Teacher's tips

Place value is an important part of maths. Your child will need to have a good understanding of the value and position of each digit in a number up to one hundred before moving on to larger numbers.

Let's practise

These numbers are made from tens and ones.

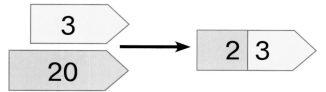

20 and 3 makes 23.

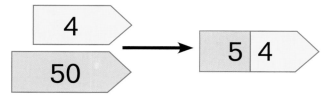

50 and 4 makes 54.
Write these numbers.

②
8
20

⑤
6
30

③
5
40

⑥
7
50

④
2
30

⑦
4
60

Have a go

⑧ Colour the shapes with
numbers between 20 and 30.
What can you see?

_____

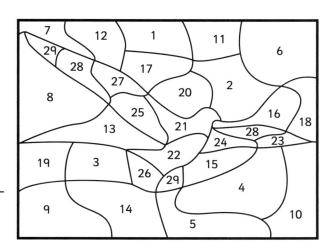

4: Addition

Charlie gave me 6 red counters and Abbie gave me 3 yellow counters. This can be written as **6+3**. The **+** sign tells you to add the numbers. Abbie says that the numbers either side of the **=** sign must be balanced and equal to each other. She placed 9 counters to show the answer.

6	+	3	=	9
6	add	3	equals	9

Get ready

Write a sum for each picture.

4   + _____ = _____

_____ + _____ = _____

_____ + _____ = _____   _____ + _____ = _____

_____ + _____ = _____   _____ + _____ = _____

Teacher's tips

Encourage your child to hold the largest number in their head and count on to find the total.

Let's practise

Draw some more fruit to help work out the missing numbers.

  +

4 + _____ = 6

8  +

5 + _____ = 8

9  +

3 + _____ = 7

10 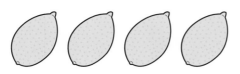 +

4 + _____ = 8

Have a go

11 Each set of additions make the same number in different ways. Write the missing numbers.

8	7	6
8 + 0		
7 + __	7 + __	6 + __
6 + __	6 + __	5 + __
5 + __	5 + 2	__ + 2
4 + __	__ + 3	3 + 3

5: Subtraction

I know there should be 6 crabs but I can only see 4 crabs. Oh, there they are – two crabs are hiding! That's just like me and Alfie!
This can be written as **6 – 2**. The **–** sign shows you have to take numbers away.

6 – 2 = 4
6 take away 2 equals 4.

Get ready

1 Draw a line from each fish to its answer.

Let's practise

Cover one fish in each set to answer these.

2 7 − 1 = _____   **5** 4 − 1 = _____

3 6 − 1 = _____   **6** 8 − 1 = _____

4 5 − 1 = _____   **7** 9 − 1 = _____

Have a go

Cover two fish in each set to answer these.

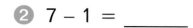

8 7 − 2 = _____   **11** 4 − 2 = _____

9 6 − 2 = _____   **12** 8 − 2 = _____

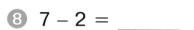

10 5 − 2 = _____   **13** 9 − 2 = _____

Count on to find the difference.

14 The difference between 2 and 5 is _____.

15 The difference between 4 and 8 is _____.

16 The difference between 5 and 10 is _____.

17 The difference between 6 and 9 is _____.

6: Multiplication

All chairs at Kids Club are very low and made for little children. Abbie is going to put longer legs on some chairs to make them higher for the older children. She has asked me to count how many legs she will need for 3 chairs. Can you help me count the legs in groups?

1 chair has 4 legs.
3 chairs have 12 legs.
3 groups of 4 make 12.

Get ready

Count the numbers in each group.

1

1 bike has _____ wheels.
3 bikes have _____ wheels.

3

1 stool has _____ legs.
4 stools have _____ legs.

2

1 glove has _____ fingers.
2 gloves have _____ fingers.

4

1 box has _____ eggs.
2 boxes have _____ eggs.

Teacher's tips

Counting in groups is a useful step towards understanding the concept of multiplication because multiplication can be represented as repeated addition. 4 groups of 3 is 3 + 3 + 3 + 3, which is 3 multiplied 4 times. When introducing the multiplication sign as 'multiplied by', it is important your child understands the concept of multiplying as grouping and repeated addition.

Your child will also learn that multiplication is commutative, which means that, for example, 3 × 5 gives the same answer as 5 × 3.

Let's practise

How many? Count these in groups.

5

_____ groups of 2 make _____.

7

_____ groups of 4 make _____.

6

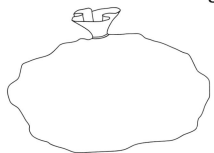

_____ groups of 3 make _____.

8

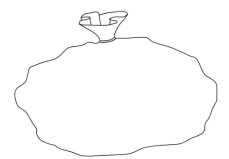

_____ groups of 4 make _____.

Have a go

9 Draw 4 balls in each bag.

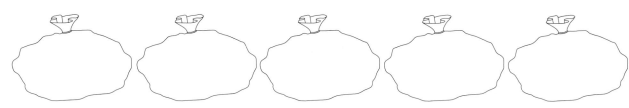

4 multiplied by 2 is _____.
4 × 2 = _____

10 Draw 3 balls in each bag.

3 multiplied by 5 is _____.
3 × 5 = _____

7: Division

At Kids Club we teach the children that it is important to share equally.

These 6 apples are shared between 2 children.
They have 3 apples each.

Get ready

Share these equally between the bags.

1

8 shared between 2 is _____.

2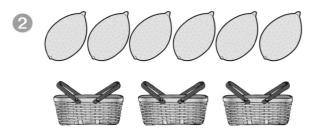

6 shared between 3 is _____.

3

12 shared between 3 is _____.

4

10 shared between 2 is _____.

Teacher's tips

Division can be represented as sharing and grouping. A child's first experience of dividing is usually equal sharing, with children physically giving out items one at a time to make sure there is equal division. However, it is important to move on from sharing to the grouping model for division as it links to repeated subtraction. For example, 12 grouped into threes to make 4 groups (12 ÷ 3 = 4) can be modelled by repeatedly subtracting groups of 3. The ÷ sign also relates better to division as grouping.

Divide these objects by putting them into equal groups.

10 grouped into twos is 5.
10 divided by 2 is 5.
10 ÷ 2 = 5

 Let's practise

⑤ Group these into twos and count the groups.

_____ groups

⑥ Group these into threes and count the groups.

_____ groups

Have a go

Colour these to show the groups.

⑦

12 grouped into threes is _____.

12 ÷ 3 = _____

⑨

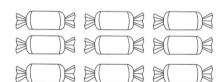

9 grouped into threes is _____.

9 ÷ 3 = _____

⑧

8 grouped into twos is _____.

8 ÷ 2 = _____

⑩

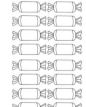

16 grouped into twos is _____.

16 ÷ 2 = _____

8: Fractions

I like playing with sticky shapes at Kids Club. I think I'll cut some into halves and quarters.

One half or $\frac{1}{2}$ of this shape is red.

$\frac{1}{2}$ shows one out of two equal parts.

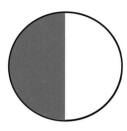

One quarter or $\frac{1}{4}$ of this shape is blue.

$\frac{1}{4}$ shows one out of four equal parts.

Get ready

1 Colour $\frac{1}{2}$ of each shape.

   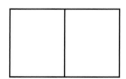

2 Colour $\frac{1}{4}$ of each shape.

Teacher's tips

Fractions can cause great difficulties for children. They can be confused by the representation of the fraction as two small numbers separated by a line. Introduce the bottom number (the denominator) as the number of parts the whole is divided into, and the top number (the numerator) as the number of those parts that are taken. The line can be explained as meaning 'divided by'. At this stage all the fraction work is practical, finding equal parts of an object, shape or quantity.

Let's practise

3 Draw a ring around one half of the stars.

$\frac{1}{2}$ of 6 is _____.

4 Draw a ring round one half of the stars.

$\frac{1}{2}$ of 10 is _____.

5 Draw a ring round one quarter of the stars.

$\frac{1}{4}$ of 8 is _____.

6 Draw a ring round one quarter of the stars.

$\frac{1}{4}$ of 12 is _____.

Have a go

$\frac{3}{4}$ of this shape is shaded.

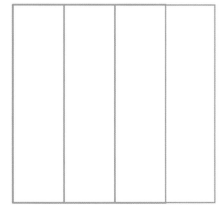

7 Shade $\frac{3}{4}$ of each of these shapes.

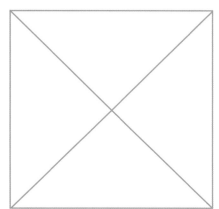

9: Shapes

Charlie has sent us on a 'shape hunt'. We're looking for objects in Kids Club that are the same shape as these.

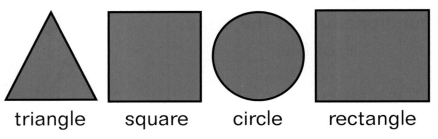

triangle   square   circle   rectangle

I've found a clock, which is a circle, and a door, which is a rectangle. It's great fun, can you find these shapes around your home?

◯ Get ready

Draw these shapes.

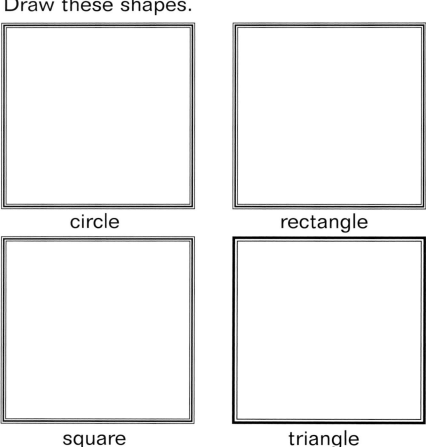

circle

rectangle

square

triangle

Teacher's tips

Your child will be starting to recognise and name some flat (2D) shapes and solid (3D) shapes. Talk about their properties, for example the shape of the faces of solid shapes or the number of sides of flat shapes. As they look at shapes and sort them, ask your child to talk about any similarities and differences between the shapes.

Try to learn the names of these shapes.

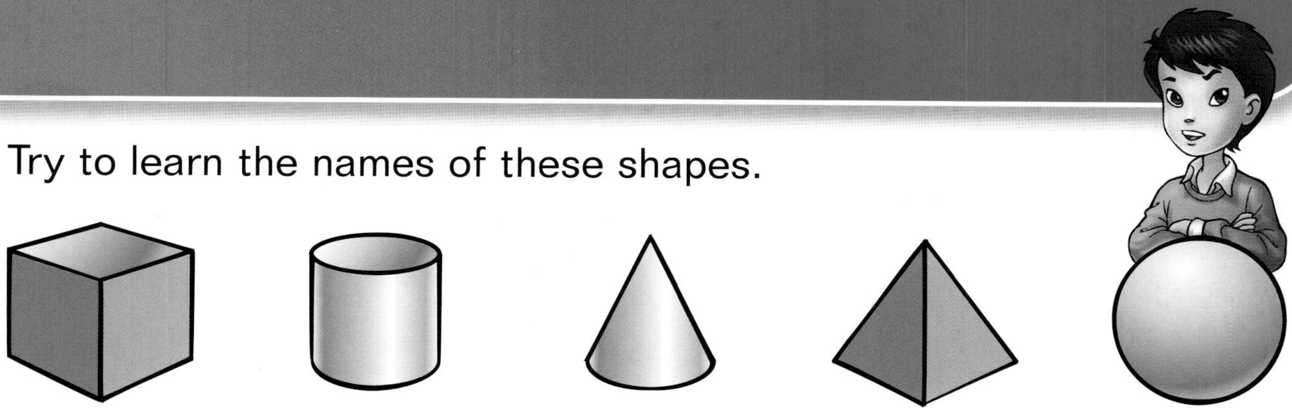

cube   cylinder   cone   pyramid   sphere

Let's practise

Join each shape to its name.

cube   cylinder   cone   sphere   pyramid

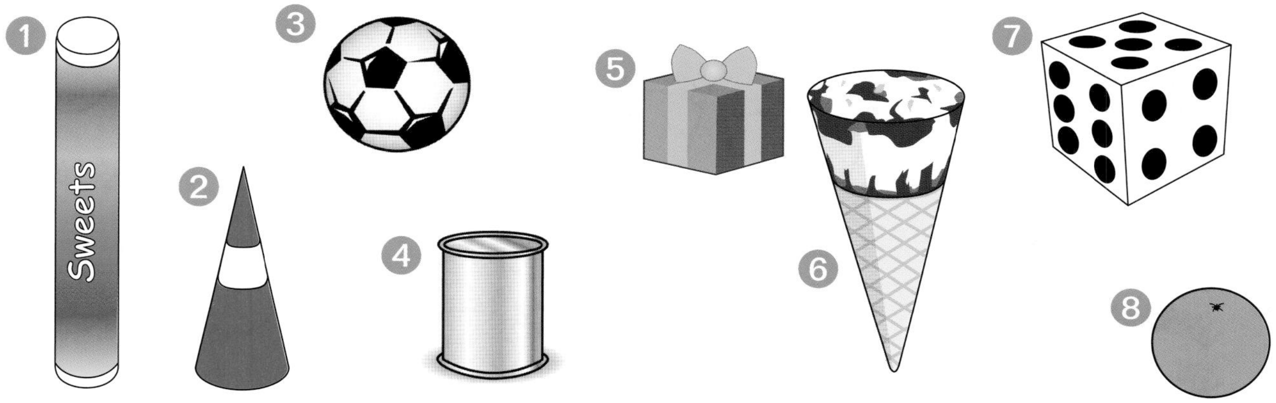

① Sweets

③

⑤

⑦

②

④

⑥

⑧

Have a go

⑨ Colour the shapes that have three sides.

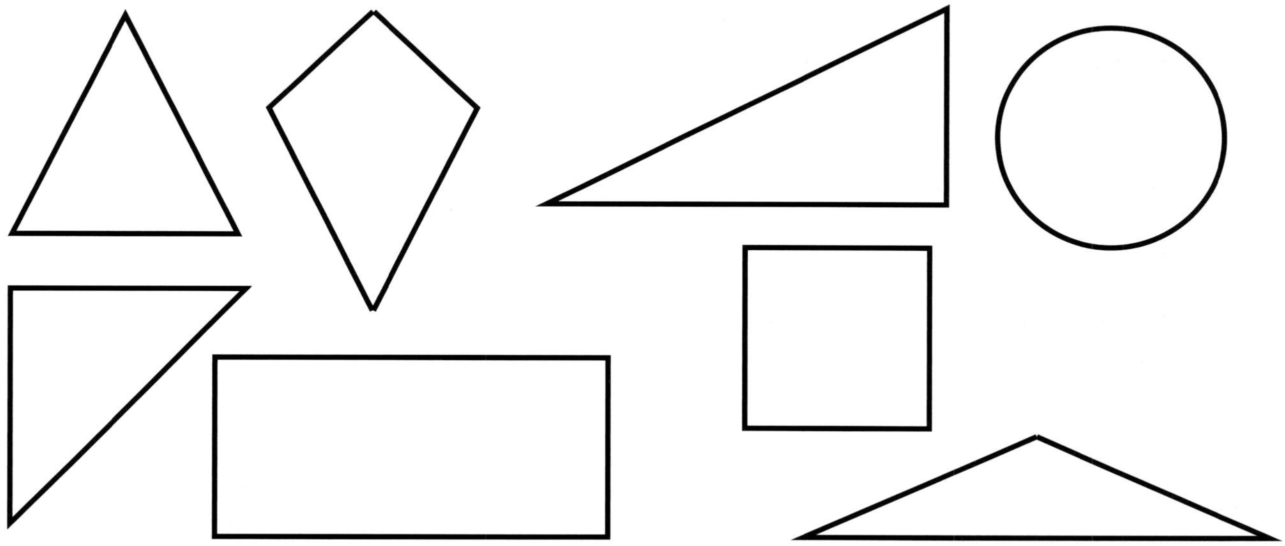

Shapes with three sides are called _____.

We are having a toy boat race at Kids Club. I will take these numbers to the pond to help us put them in order.

Get ready

Write each set of numbers in order on the flags.

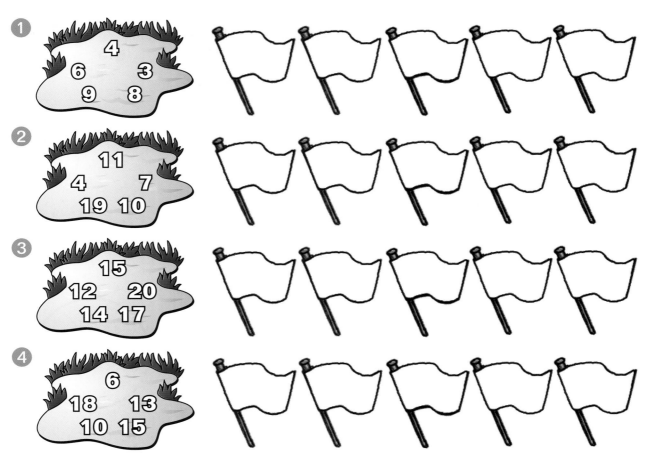

Teacher's tips

Ordering is an important skill to develop with your child. Your child should be able to compare two numbers and say which is bigger or smaller. Use number lines or tracks to reinforce the order of numbers. Use first, second, third... (the ordinal numbers) in everyday situations, for example when playing, reading or shopping.

5 The race has started! Colour the boats to match the order in the race.

    1st 2nd 3rd 4th 5th

Have a go

Draw lines to join each set of coins in order of value, starting with the lowest.

6

7

11: Time

I read the time on a clock to know when to open Kids Club.
This clock shows 3 o'clock.
Kids Club opens at 3.00.

3.00

This clock shows 30 minutes later.
It is now half past three.
3.30 is when school finishes.

3.30

Get ready

Match these clocks to the correct times.

four o'clock	one o'clock	half past eleven	half past five

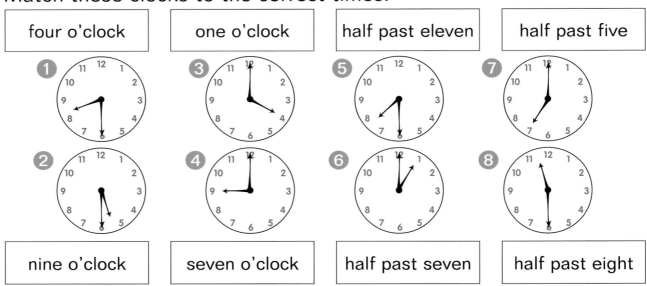

nine o'clock	seven o'clock	half past seven	half past eight

Teacher's tips

Time can be a difficult concept to understand, and telling the time is a difficult skill.
Your child will be beginning to know the days of the week and reading times to
the hour and half hour. Reinforce the fact that the hour hand is the short one, for
example by telling your child that 'hour' is a short word compared to 'minute'. They
also need experience of sequences of time and order through the day.

Let's practise

9 Write the days of the week in order.

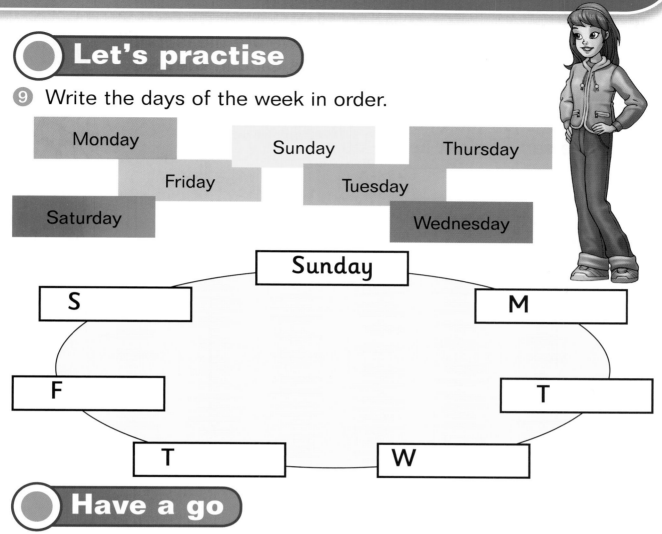

Monday Sunday Thursday

Friday Tuesday

Saturday Wednesday

Sunday

S

M

F

T

T

W

Have a go

These stories are muddled up.
Put numbers underneath to show the right order.

10

11

12

12: Measures

Abbie has given us a metre stick and we are measuring the height and length of things at Kids Club in **metres**.

This door is 2 metres high.
I am shorter than the door, Charlie is nearly the same height as the door.

These scales measure mass in **kilograms**.
Here is 2 kilograms of flour.
I am heavier than this flour, I weigh 25 kilograms.

This jug measures capacity in **litres**.
Here is 2 litres of water.
A glass holds less water than this jug.
This jug of water would fill 4 glasses.

 Get ready

These pieces of ribbon are all different lengths. Join them to the correct lengths.

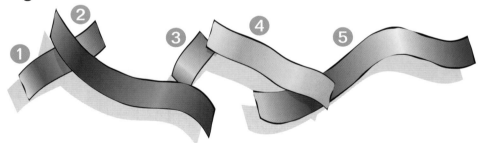

| 1 metre | 2 metres | 3 metres | 4 metres | 5 metres |

Teacher's tips

Use the language of comparison to describe length, mass and capacity of different objects, such as longer, shorter, taller, heavier, lighter, more than, less than, full, empty etc.

The units of metres, centimetres, grams, kilograms, millilitres and litres are introduced to give some sort of standard measure. Give your child the opportunity to handle, compare and measure objects so that they recognise the value of these units of measure.

Let's practise

6 Join these in order. Start with the smallest capacity.

Have a go

Which is heavier? Circle it.

7

9

8

10

1 Write each number as a word.
a) 15 → _____   b) 20 → _____

2 Count how many and write the number. _____

3 Write the missing number.

9	10	11	12		14

4 Draw a line and join these numbers in order.

30   70   20

10   90   40   100

60   50   80

5 Write the number made from these tens and ones.

 7

_____

40

6 Write a sum for this picture.

___   +   ___   =   _____

7 6 + 6 = ___

8 Cover two fish and answer this.
9 − 2 = _____

9 Circle the take away that gives 4 as the answer.

 8 − 7   6 − 4   9 − 5   7 − 2

10 Count in groups and complete this.

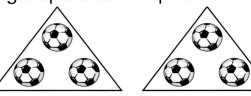

___ groups of 3 make ___.

⑪ 12 shared between 3 is ____.

⑫ 14 grouped into twos is _____.

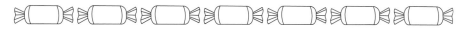

14 ÷ 2 = ___

⑬ Colour ¼ of this circle.

⑭ ½ of 8 is ____

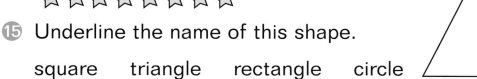

⑮ Underline the name of this shape.

square   triangle   rectangle   circle

⑯ Circle the shape that is a cylinder.

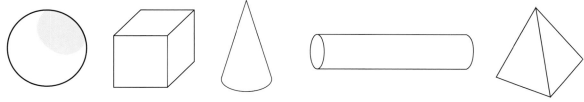

⑰ Write this set of numbers in order.

___   ___   ___   ___   ___

⑱ Write the time on this clock.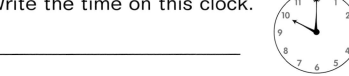

_____

⑲ Tick the clock that shows half past two.

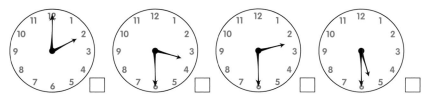

⑳ Circle the container that holds the smallest capacity.

Solving Problems

Fun problem solving questions

We are setting up some games for the Kids Club. Can you answer these questions?

1. How many pairs of table-tennis bats are there? _____

2. Jamelia needs double the number of hoops. What is the total she needs? _____

3. Amina needs half the number of footballs. How many footballs does Amina need? _____

4. Megan needs double the amount of skipping ropes. How many ropes is that? _____

Let's practise

Here is the score-sheet for penalty practice.
Can you double these scores?

		SCORE	DOUBLED
5	Megan	5	
6	Jamelia	7	
7	Amina	3	
8	Alfie	8	
9	Kim	6	

Can you halve these scores for playing hoops?

		SCORE	HALVED
10	Megan	8	
11	Jamelia	14	
12	Amina	4	
13	Alfie	12	
14	Kim	22	

Have a go

Kim, Jamelia and Megan ran a race. Kim ran it in 20 seconds. Jamelia ran it in half his time. Megan ran the race in double his time. Who won the race?

Teacher's tips

To double a number you times it by 2, or add it to itself. So double 4 is 4 × 2, or 4 + 4. A 'pair' is another word for a set of 2 – think of a 'pair' of shoes.

2: Addition problems

Hi, children! I'd like you to help me with the snacks today. Can you add these up for me? You could use cubes or your fingers to help you.

● Get ready

①   4 biscuits plus 1 more biscuit = _____ biscuits altogether

②   5 apples add 2 apples = _____ apples altogether

③   2 bananas add 4 bananas = _____ bananas altogether

④   3 oranges add 3 more = _____ oranges altogether

⑤   4 cakes plus 4 more = _____ cakes altogether

Let's practise

Can you help me add up the cartons of juice?

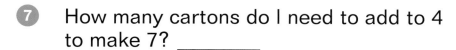

6 2 cartons added to 3 cartons equals how many altogether? _____

7 How many cartons do I need to add to 4 to make 7? _____

8 What is the sum of 5 cartons and 5 cartons? _____

9 What is 3 cartons plus 4 cartons? _____

10 Add 6 cartons to 1 carton. _____

This is what some of the children had to eat and drink. Can you answer the questions?

11 Megan had 6 crisps. Amina gave her 4 more. How many crisps did Megan have in total? _____

12 Kim had 18 biscuits. Alfie has 3 more than Kim. How many biscuits does Alfie have? _____

Have a go

Count all the books you have in your bedroom. Count all the soft toys. How many books and soft toys do you have altogether? You could give the ones you don't need any more to the charity shop!

Teacher's tips

When a question is written in words, underline the *quantities* and *actions* then write them as numbers and maths symbols above. This makes it easier to see the maths question that's being asked.

We are sorting out the pencil pots for some of the tables. Would you like to help us?

Get ready

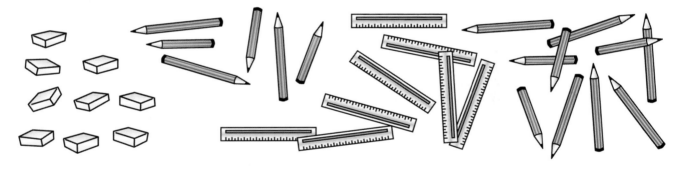

1. There are 9 rubbers. Jamelia gives 1 to Amina. How many rubbers are left? _____

2. There are 6 blue pencils. Amina gives 1 to Alfie. How many blue pencils are left? _____

3. There are 8 rulers. I give 1 to Kim. How many rulers are left?

   _____

4. There are 10 red pencils. Kim gives 1 to Amina. How many red pencils are left? _____

Let's practise

First find the bigger number, then count back to get the answer.

(5) There are 7 green pencils in the pot but I drop 2. How many are left in the pot? _____

(6) There are 12 felt-tip pens in the cupboard. Abbie puts 10 in the pot. How many are left in the cupboard? _____

(7) There are 11 crayons in the box. Alfie puts 7 in the pot. How many crayons are left in the box? _____

(8) Jamelia has 10 pencil sharpeners. She gives 8 to put in the pots. How many does she have left? _____

(9) Amina has 9 rubbers. She gives 7 to put in the pots. How many does she have left? _____

(10) Alfie takes 8 pencils from Jamelia who has 15. How many pencils does Jamelia have now? _____

(11) Amina has 21 rulers. I have 7 less than her. How many rulers do I have? _____

Have a go

Ask a grown-up to say a number between 5 and 20. Take 5 off the number. How fast can you answer? Practise until you are lightning quick! Try changing the numbers – both what the grown-up says and the number you must take off.

Teacher's tips

Translate the question into a number sentence to help work out the answer. They are all subtraction questions so will read "number – number = answer".

We have brought in some toys to show at Kids Club.

These are my toy cars. How many are there altogether?

$5 + 5 + 5 + 5 = 20$ or $4 + 4 + 4 + 4 + 4 = 20$

or $\qquad$ $5 \times 4 = 20$ $\qquad$ or $\qquad$ $4 \times 5 = 20$

Counting in groups is multiplying.

Get ready

1. 3 lots of 3 cars is how many cars altogether? _____

2. 4 times 2 dolls is how many dolls in total? _____

3. 2 groups of 6 teddies equals how many teddies? _____

4. How many marbles in 2 groups of 2 marbles? _____

5. How many is 5 times 2 stickers? _____

Now try these.

6 How many soldiers in 5 lots of 5 toy soldiers? _____

7 How many is 3 robots multiplied by 6? _____

8 6 multiplied by how many dinosaurs equals 24 dinosaurs? _____

9 How many puppets in 2 groups of 9 puppets? _____

10 How many footballs in 7 groups of 4 footballs? _____

Have a go

If Jamelia, Amina, Alfie, Megan and Kim each brought in their six favourite toys to put on display, how many toys would be in the display?

Draw this number of toys on a sheet of paper. Display it as a poster. Make it as attractive as you can.

Teacher's tips

Write out the question as a number sentence, using the multiplication symbol × for 'lots of', 'multiplied by' and 'groups of'.

5: Division problems

We all share our things at Kids Club. That way everyone stays happy!

Get ready

1. Share 6 sweets equally between Jamelia and Megan. How many do they get each? _____

2. Share 6 sweets equally among Amina, myself and Kim. How many do we get each? _____

3. Share 10 sweets equally among all 5 children. How many do we get each? _____

4. Share 10 sweets equally between Abbie and Charlie. How many do they get each? _____

5. A bar of chocolate has 8 squares. How many squares can Amina and Kim have each if they are shared equally? _____

Let's practise

Now answer these. You could try drawing your answers on a blank piece of paper to help you.

6 There are 18 books on a shelf. How many bags of 3 books can be filled? _____

7 I have 24 football stickers. How many sets of 4 can I give away? _____

8 How many sticks of 4 cubes can Kim make from a stick of 20 cubes? _____

9 If Megan counted in tens from 0 to 60, how many tens would she count? _____

10 How many groups of 2 CDs make up Jamelia's collection of 8? _____

The Kids Club record for doing these calculations is 10 seconds. Jamelia holds the record but see if you can beat her!

11 $10 \div 2 =$ ☐ **12** $20 \div$ ☐ $= 2$ **13** ☐ $\div 10 = 3$

14 $28 \div 4 =$ ☐ **15** ☐ $\div 3 = 8$

Have a go

Take a box of things like buttons or safety matches. Divide them into groups of 2, then 3, then 4 and finally 5. Which groups did they divide into exactly? Which ones have a remainder? Record your results on a piece of paper.

Teacher's tips

When dividing numbers or groups of objects each of the smaller groups must contain the same number of objects. ÷ means 'shared equally between'.

6: Problems in measure (1)

We have been collecting things from the woods.

Now we are going to record and measure them for our nature table. I'd love it if you could help!

● Get ready

Draw a line from each item to the correct unit of measurement. The first one has been done for you.

Weight of a log ————————— grams

1. Capacity of an empty shell   kilograms

2. Width of a pine cone   metres

3. Weight of a bird's nest   centimetres

4. Capacity of a small pond   millilitres

5. Length of a fallen tree   litres

Let's practise

Now try to answer these questions on weight, length and capacity.

Weight: Would you measure these things in grams or kilograms?
Tick the correct box.

6 a) b) c)

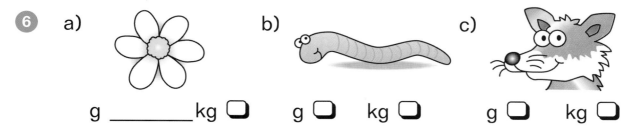

g _____ kg ⬭   g ⬭   kg ⬭   g ⬭   kg ⬭

Length: Would you measure these things in centimetres or
metres? Tick the correct box.

7 a) b) c)

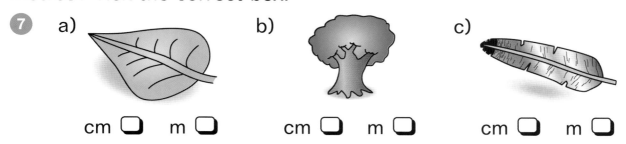

cm ⬭   m ⬭   cm ⬭   m ⬭   cm ⬭   m ⬭

Capacity: Would you measure the capacity of these containers in
millilitres or litres? Tick the correct box.

8 a) b) c)

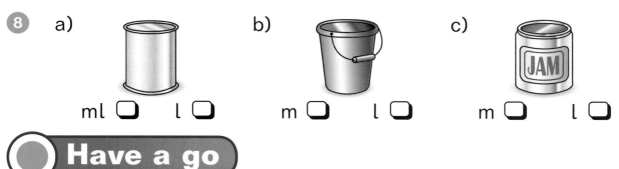

ml ⬭   l ⬭   m ⬭   l ⬭   m ⬭   l ⬭

Have a go

Alfie has found an old lunch box. It is very like yours at home.
Find a plastic lunch box and measure its length, weight and
capacity.

Teacher's tips

Learn the meanings of milli (one-thousandth of a__), centi (one-hundredth of a__)
and kilo (one thousand) to help you work out which unit of measurement to use for
large and small items.

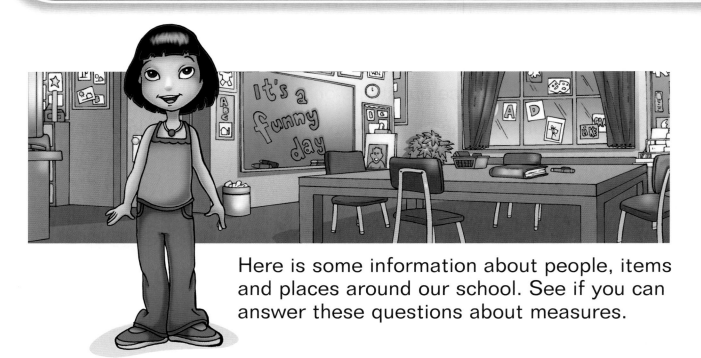

Here is some information about people, items and places around our school. See if you can answer these questions about measures.

Get ready

1 The classroom is 15m long. The school kitchen is 10m long. How much longer is the classroom than the kitchen? _____

2 The library is 20m long. The gym is 30m long. How much longer is the gym than the library? _____

3 Jamelia and Alfie are both on the scales. 6 blocks balance Jamelia. 8 blocks balance A lfie. How many blocks are needed to balance them? _____

4 Megan and Abbie are both on the scales. 7 blocks balance Megan. 12 blocks balance Abbie. How many blocks are needed to balance them? _____

5 A full kettle of water holds 10 cups of water. How many cups of water do 2 kettles hold? _____

6 A full jug holds 14 cups of water. How many cups of water do 2 jugs hold? _____

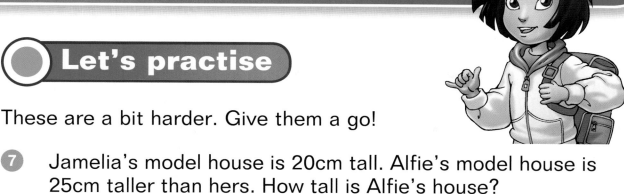

Let's practise

These are a bit harder. Give them a go!

7 Jamelia's model house is 20cm tall. Alfie's model house is 25cm taller than hers. How tall is Alfie's house? _____

8 Abbie has 5kg of fruit in one box. How many kilograms of fruit would there be in 3 of these boxes? _____

9 I have 50 litres of water in my bath. How many 10 litre buckets can I fill? _____

10 Megan has a garden wall that is 50cm high. Kim's garden wall is 25cm higher. How high is Kim's garden wall? _____

11 Alfie has 10kg of sand in his sandpit. How many kilograms of sand would there be in 4 sandpits? _____

12 Abbie needs 32 litres of petrol for her car. How many 4 litre cans of petrol would this be? _____

13 Jamelia has a piece of string that is 25cm long. Alfie cuts off 11cm and then Kim cuts off 9cm. How long is Jamelia's piece of string now? _____

14 Abbie has 7 litres of soup. She adds 8 more litres and the children eat 3 litres. How much soup is left? _____

Have a go

Find a recipe for making pizza dough. Use the Internet or a book. Ask a grown-up to help you measure the correct ingredients and then try and make a pizza. Add your favourite toppings! How much of each ingredient would you need for two pizzas?

Teacher's tips

Underline the *quantities* and *actions* as before, but this time make sure you use the right units of measurement when writing the answer.

8: Problems in measure (3)

We are going to look at reading scales on different pieces of measuring equipment.

Get ready

What do these instruments show?

1

0 cm 1 2 3 4 5 6 7 8 9 10 11 12 13 14 15 16 17 18 19 20 21 22 23 24 25 26 27 28 29 30

_____ cm

2

0 cm 1 2 3 4 5 6 7 8 9 10 11 12 13 14 15 16 17 18 19 20 21 22 23 24 25 26 27 28 29 30

_____ cm

3 _____ g

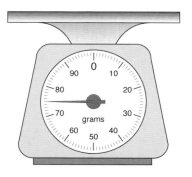

4 _____ ml

Let's practise

Ask a grown-up for a ruler, a set of scales and a measuring jug.

5 Measure these worms to the nearest centimetre.

_____ cm

_____ cm

6 Using a set of kitchen scales, measure the weight of these household objects. Write your results in the box below.

ITEM	WEIGHT (g)	ITEM	WEIGHT (g)
An apple		Your shoe	
A CD		A book	

7 Using a measuring jug and water, measure the capacity of these kitchen items. Write your results in the box below.

ITEM	CAPACITY (ml)
A mug	
A cereal bowl	
A glass	

Have a go

Investigate how tall and how heavy you are. Record your results. Do the same for the rest of your family. Try guessing first!

Teacher's tips

When measuring always start at zero – so, using a ruler, one end of the object being measured must be held against the '0' on the ruler. With scales, the reading before an object is added must always be zero.

9: Money problems

Knowing about money is very useful. Here are all the coins we use.

Get ready

We are going to buy some items for Kids Club. How much are they?

1. Milk   _____

2. Biscuits     _____

3. Tea   _____

4. Squash    _____

Let's practise

We want to buy some new toys for Kids Club. Can you help us at the toy shop?

5   I have £15. Abbie gives me £9 more. How much do I have now? _____

6   A bouncy ball costs 16p more than a marble. A marble costs 12p. What does a bouncy ball cost?

_____

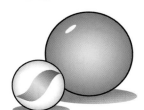

7   Alfie spent 34p on stink bombs! He spent 9p more than Megan. How much did Megan spend? _____

8   Amina bought 3 stickers at 15p each. How much change did Amina get from 50p? _____

9   I spend £8 on a board game. How much change do I get from £10? _____

10   Abbie spends 92p on some coloured beads. How much change does she get from a £2 coin? _____

Have a go

Look at ways of using silver coins (5p, 10p, 20p, 50p) to pay for a colouring book that costs 95p. How many ways can you think of to pay?

Teacher's tips

Think about whether the answer is going to be *more* or *less*. Checking if your answer is what you expected is a good way to see if you've made a mistake when it's a tricky question.

Hopscotch is a popular game in the playground. We love playing it at Kids Club. However, someone has rubbed out some of the numbers in the hopscotch squares!

Get ready

Can you fill in the squares with the correct numbers?
Using a hundred square will help you find the answers.

1. 12 — 13 — 14 — ☐ — ☐ — ☐

2. 28 — 29 — 30 — ☐ — ☐ — ☐

3. 47 — 48 — 49 — ☐ — ☐ — ☐

4. 10 — 20 — 30 — ☐ — ☐ — ☐

I think it might have been Alfie who rubbed out the numbers! See if you can help us to fill in the rest of the missing numbers.

5 | 22 | 24 | 26 | | |

6 | 17 | 19 | 21 | | |

7 | 33 | 36 | 39 | | |

8 | 47 | 50 | 53 | | |

9 | 61 | 66 | 71 | | |

10 | 98 | 94 | 90 | | |

11 | 50 | 45 | 40 | | |

12 | 25 | 35 | 45 | | |

13 | 81 | 75 | 69 | | |

14 | 6 | 15 | 24 | | |

Have a go

Try to find some examples of number sequences. House numbers are a good start. Make a list of the ones you find. What would the next numbers be in the sequences?

Teacher's tips

Write down between each number the maths action that has happened to change the number (for example to go from 22 to 24 you have added 2, '+2'). Do the same action each time to complete the pattern.

All the children at Kids Club have learnt to tell the time. Have you?
Kids Club lasts from 3.30pm to 6.00pm. That is $2\frac{1}{2}$ hours.

Can you answer these questions about time?

Get ready

1 How long is it from 3.00pm to 6.00pm?

2 If lunchtime starts at 12.00pm and lasts one hour, at what time does it finish?

Draw the following times on these clock faces.

3 9 o'clock

4 6 o'clock

5 2 o'clock

Let's practise

Here are some questions about how we spend our time at Kids Club.

6 On Mondays, Jamelia starts Kids Club at 3.30pm and gets picked up 30 minutes later. At what time does Jamelia get picked up?

_____

7 On Tuesdays, I listen to a story from 5.45pm until 6.00pm. How long am I listening for?_____

8 On Wednesdays, Amina plays with the pet hamster from 4.45pm until 5.15pm. How many minutes does Amina play with the hamster for? _____

9 On Thursdays, Kim makes clay models from 4.00pm until 5.00pm. How many minutes is that? _____

10 On Fridays, Alfie helps make the drinks and snacks. It takes him 15 minutes. Write down two times that he could do this between. _____

Have a go

Write down the time you go to bed and the time you get up. How many hours do you spend in bed each night? How many hours is this for a whole week? What about the rest of your family?

Teacher's tips

When we write times, the number before the '.' is the hour, and the number after is how many minutes past that hour it is. As there are 60 minutes in an hour not 100, we have to remember to start at .00 again after 60 minutes (not 99!).

12: Puzzles and problems

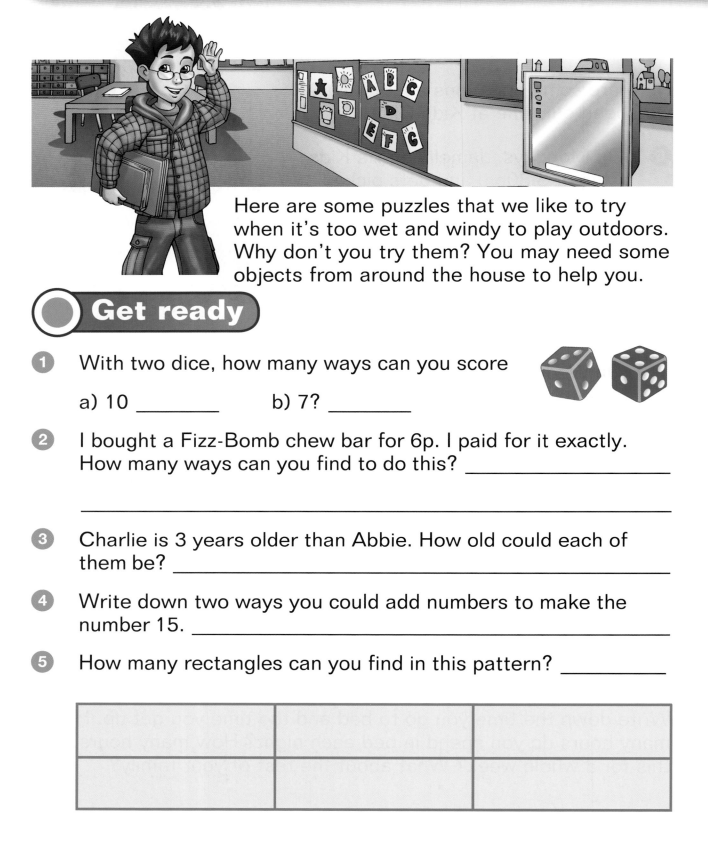

Here are some puzzles that we like to try when it's too wet and windy to play outdoors. Why don't you try them? You may need some objects from around the house to help you.

Get ready

1 With two dice, how many ways can you score

 a) 10 _____ b) 7? _____

2 I bought a Fizz-Bomb chew bar for 6p. I paid for it exactly. How many ways can you find to do this? _____

_____

3 Charlie is 3 years older than Abbie. How old could each of them be? _____

4 Write down two ways you could add numbers to make the number 15. _____

5 How many rectangles can you find in this pattern? _____

Let's practise

These are a little harder. Give them a go!

6   With three dice, how many ways can you score 11? _____

7   Three dinosaurs laid some eggs. Each dinosaur laid an odd number of eggs. They laid 19 altogether. How many eggs did each dinosaur lay? Can you find ten ways?

_____

_____

8   Write down two ways you could add up numbers to make the number 25. _____

9   Kim bought an ice cream using only silver coins. It cost 55p. How could Kim have paid for it?

_____

10   What colour is each of these shapes? Write it on the shape.

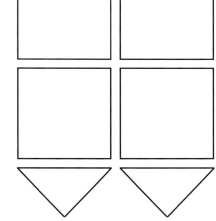

Clues: Blue is not next to grey.
Red is between white and grey.
Yellow is not a square.
Red is on the right of pink.

Have a go

Cut up two different birthday or Christmas cards into eight pieces and shuffle them. Can you put the two pictures back together again?

Teacher's tips

With tricky questions it's always good to try out a few ideas on a piece of paper first to see what works and what doesn't – experiment with different methods!

How have I done?

Answer these questions to see how well you have done at Kids Club.

1 Amina has 11 comics. Megan has double that number. How many comics does Megan have? _____

2 Alfie has 18 conkers. Jamelia has half that number. How many conkers does Jamelia have? _____

3 Kim has 9 marbles. Amina has 5 marbles more than him. How many marbles does Amina have? _____

4 What is the sum of 12 and 13? _____

5 Alfie has 20 sweets and eats 14. How many does he have left? _____

6 Megan has 17 chocolate fingers. Jamelia has 15 chocolate fingers. What is the difference between the two? _____

7 How many is 8 multiplied by 4? _____

8 Kim has 5 groups of 6 toy soldiers. How many toy soldiers does he have in total? _____

9 There are 16 drinks. How many groups of 4 are there? _____

10 Amina shares 20 stickers equally among 4 friends. How many stickers does each friend receive? _____

11 Tick the box for the one you would use to measure the weight of a cake.

A ruler ▢   A set of scales ▢

12 Would you measure the length of a pencil case in metres or centimetres? _____

13 Alfie has 40 litres of water in his paddling pool. How many 10 litre buckets can he fill? _____

14. Megan has 12 biscuits in a packet. How many biscuits are there in 2 packets? _____

15. How much water is in this measuring jug? _____

16. Alfie has caught this fish! How long is it, to the nearest centimetre? _____

17. Jamelia has £10 birthday money. She spends £4 on a pet hamster. How much does she have left? _____

18. Amina bought 4 apples at 10p each. How much change did Amina get from 50p? _____

19. What are the next two numbers in this sequence?
23 20 17 ____ ____

20. Complete Kim's number pattern.
21 25 29 ____ ____

21. Draw 8 o'clock on this clock face.

22. Megan goes to bed at 7.30pm. She gets up 11 hours later. At what time does Megan get up? _____

23. How many legs are there on two chairs? _____

24. Which is heavier, a kilogram of pebbles or a kilogram of feathers? Tick the box you think is correct.

pebbles ☐   feathers ☐   weigh the same ☐

Total ____
        24

Well done for working so hard. We hope you've enjoyed your time at Kids Club!

Teacher's tips

When you do a test, have a sheet of paper to write down your notes and your working out. If you're not sure about a question leave it out and come back to it at the end.

Mental Maths

Build mental maths skills

This afternoon we are counting up the gold stars that the children have earned. Some of them have done really well. Help the children count their stars.

Get ready

1. Megan has 6 + 4 = ☐ stars.

2. Alfie has 2 + 6 = ☐ stars.

3. Jamelia has 8 + 3 = ☐ stars.

4. Amina has 10 + 5 = ☐ stars.

5. Kim has 13 + 7 = ☐ stars.

6. Who has the most stars? _____

7. Who has the least stars? _____

Let's practise

Now add up last week's star totals.

8 Amina had 15 + 9 = ☐ stars.

9 Kim had 20 + 7 = ☐ stars.

10 Megan had 10 + 18 = ☐ stars.

11 Alfie had 10 + 20 = ☐ stars.

12 Jamelia had 11 + 11 = ☐ stars.

13 Who had the most stars? _____

14 Who had the least stars? _____

15 What was the total of Alfie's and Amina's stars? _____

16 What was the total of Alfie's and Jamelia's stars? _____

Have a go

Write down the names and ages of yourself and other members of your family.

What is the total age of you and any brothers and sisters?

What is the total age of you and the grown-ups in your home?

What is the total age of your family?

Teacher's tips

Addition can be done in any order so start with the biggest number. Put it 'in your head' and then add the smaller number to it by counting on (use your fingers if it helps).

2: Addition (2)

We have been learning the language of addition. It's not just the word 'add', you know! All these words are to do with addition.

more	add	plus	sum	total	altogether

The sign for addition is '+' and the sign for equals is '='. The equals sign shows you where to put your answer.

Get ready

1. What is 3 add 6? _____

2. Add 5 and 4. _____

3. What is 9 plus 5? _____

4. What is the total of 12 and 8? _____

5. What is the sum of 7 and 11? _____

6. How many are 10 and 13 altogether? _____

7. What must Megan add to 7 to make 10? _____

8. Alfie thinks of a number. He adds 5. The answer is 8. What number was Alfie thinking of? _____

Let's practise

Now try these questions.

9   What is 37 add 10? _____

10 Add 50 to 40. _____

11 What is 9 plus 18? _____

12 What is the sum of 18 and 9? _____

13 What is the total of 16 and 7? _____

14 How many are 5 and 17 altogether? _____

15 Which two numbers could have a total of 14? _____

16 What must I add to 18 to make 20? _____

17 I think of a number. I add 10. The answer is 40. What is my number? _____

18 I think of a new number. I add 12. The answer is 20. What is my number? _____

Have a go

Using the words in the box on the opposite page, make a poster about addition. Write the word 'addition' in the middle and put all the other words around it.

Use the plus sign (+) and equals sign (=) on your poster.

Make up some addition calculations for your poster using animals or objects.

You could give your poster to a younger child or put it on your wall.

Teacher's tips

Write the question out as a number sentence before you try to solve it. So 37 add 10 becomes 37 + 10 = ?

We have brought some money to spend at the disco. We can buy sweets, fruit, nuts and drinks.

Here is what we bought. How much did each of us spend?

10p SWEETS

5p each

15p Nuts

8p

Get ready

1. Kim bought sweets, nuts and a banana.

2. I bought nuts, juice and an orange.

3. Alfie bought sweets, juice and another lot of sweets.

4. Amina bought juice, an apple and another cup of juice.

5. Jamelia bought nuts, sweets and juice.

Let's practise

This is how much each of us spent on cakes at the cake stall.

Add up the totals. Use a number line, coins or a hundred square to help you.

6 Kim spent 36p, 17p and 29p. ☐

7 I, Megan, spent 15p, 32p and 45p. ☐

8 Alfie spent 12p, 38p and 24p. ☐

9 Amina spent 33p, 14p and 31p. ☐

10 Jamelia spent 34p, 16p and 21p. ☐

11 Who spent the most money on cakes? _____

12 What is the total amount of money spent by Kim and Jamelia on cakes? _____

13 What is the total amount spent on cakes by myself, Alfie and Amina? _____

Have a go

There are 100 pence in a pound. If you buy a book for 42p, explore the number of ways you can spend the rest of the pound exactly. Look at this example:

42p + 28p + 30p = £1 (100p)

How many ways can you find?

Teacher's tips

Write the question as a number sentence again, but this time it will have 3 numbers (for example 36p + 17p + 29p = ?). Start by adding the first 2 numbers together (36p + 17p). Then add the third number (29p) to this to get the final answer.

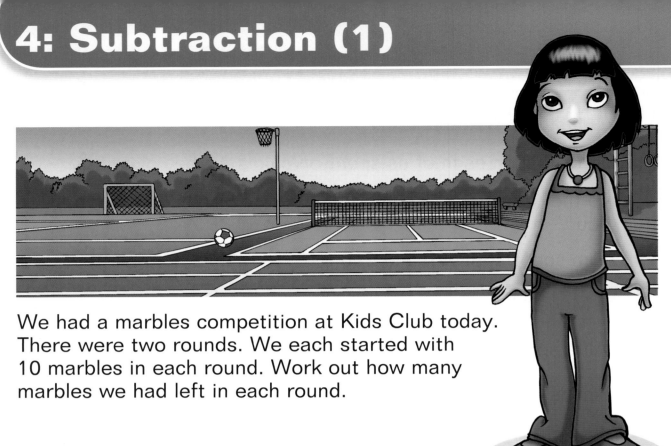

We had a marbles competition at Kids Club today. There were two rounds. We each started with 10 marbles in each round. Work out how many marbles we had left in each round.

Get ready

Round 1:

1. Megan: 10 − 2 =
2. Amina: 10 − 5 =
3. Alfie: 10 − 10 =
4. Jamelia: 10 − 0 =
5. Kim: 10 − 3 =

Round 2:

6. Megan: 10 − 8 =
7. Amina: 10 − 4 =
8. Alfie: 10 − 1 =
9. Jamelia: 10 − 6 =
10. Kim: 10 − 7 =

11. Who lost the smallest number of marbles after both rounds?

_____

Let's practise

Here are the scores from another marbles game.

Round 1:

(12) Megan: $18 - 6 =$ ☐

(13) Amina: $25 - 9 =$ ☐

(14) Alfie: $17 - 8 =$ ☐

(15) Jamelia: $28 - 5 =$ ☐

(16) Kim: $27 - 7 =$ ☐

Round 2:

(17) Megan: $39 - 8 =$ ☐

(18) Amina: $52 - 5 =$ ☐

(19) Alfie: $50 - 20 =$ ☐

(20) Jamelia: $78 - 9 =$ ☐

(21) Kim: $80 - 30 =$ ☐

(22) Who had the most marbles left after both rounds?

_____

Have a go

Imagine you have 20 pence. Here is a Kids Club list of things for sale:

Comic: 10p
Chocolate bar: 12p
Chews: 2p
Notebook: 8p
Pencil: 5p

How many ways can you spend your 20p? Record your results.

Teacher's tips

When starting with 10 or 20, remember your number bonds to help you work out the answer quickly. For harder problems use a number line or number square to help. To find out who had the most marbles at the end you need to add both answers together.

5: Subtraction (2)

Charlie asked me if I liked to take away. I said that fish and chips was my favourite. He meant take-away sums! Here are some words we use when talking about subtraction.

subtract	take away	difference between
how much less is		how many are left

Try these questions.

1. What is 5 take away 2? _____

2. Take 3 from 7. _____

3. What is 9 subtract 3? _____

4. What is 8 less than 9? _____

5. What is the difference between 15 and 12? _____

6. How much less than 8 is 4? _____

7. How much less than 5 is 3? _____

8. 8 taken from a number leaves 2. What is the number? _____

9. What number must I take from 13 to leave 10? _____

10. I think of a number. I take away 2. My answer is 9. What is my number? _____

Let's practise

Now try these questions. They are a little harder so read them carefully.

11 Take 40 from 70. _____

12 What is 21 subtract 3? _____

13 Subtract 30 from 90. _____

14 What is 7 less than 13? _____

15 What number must I take from 18 to leave 4? _____

16 What is the difference between 11 and 17? _____

17 How many are left if I take 4 from 10? _____

18 How much less than 15 is 6? _____

19 5 taken from a number is 14. What is the number? _____

20 What number must I take from 27 to leave 17? _____

Have a go

Get used to using the language of subtraction. On a large piece of paper, write down the phrases in the box on the opposite page. Put the minus sign (−) and equals sign (=) on as well. Make up your own questions like the ones here. Write them on the paper. Test a friend or a grown-up!

Teacher's tips

Write the question as a number sentence before you try to solve it. Use a '?' to show the number you need to calculate. You need to think really carefully about what the number sentence will be, some are very tricky so don't get caught out!

6: Subtraction and addition

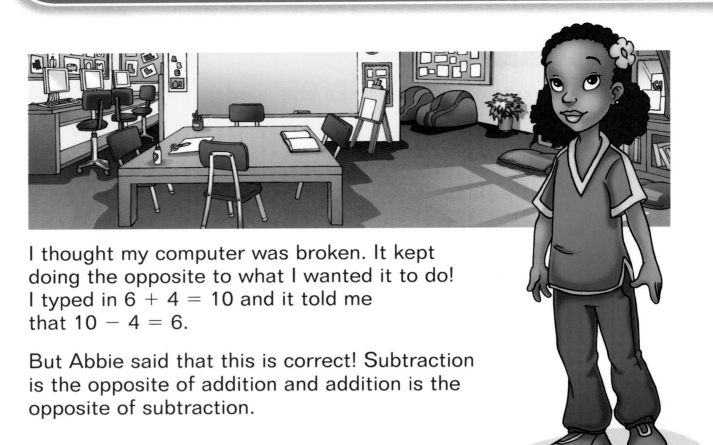

I thought my computer was broken. It kept doing the opposite to what I wanted it to do! I typed in 6 + 4 = 10 and it told me that 10 − 4 = 6.

But Abbie said that this is correct! Subtraction is the opposite of addition and addition is the opposite of subtraction.

● Get ready

Write the opposite subtraction sum to each of these calculations.

Here is an example:

3 + 5 = 8   so   8 − 5 = 3

1 4 + 5 = 9 so _____

2 3 + 7 = 10 so _____

3 8 + 6 = 14 so _____

4 10 + 5 = 15 so _____

5 12 + 2 = 14 so _____

6 27 + 3 = 30 so _____

7 22 + 1 = 23 so _____

8 28 + 5 = 33 so _____

Let's practise

So my computer is fine! Now write the opposite subtraction sum to these questions. I did one for you on my computer:

24 + 5 = 29

so

29 - 5 = 24

⑨   42 + 10 = 52 so _____

⑩   62 + 8 = 70 so _____

⑪   38 + 7 = 45 so _____

⑫   54 + 20 = 74 so _____

⑬   28 + 9 = 37 so _____

⑭   Write the opposite calculation to this sum:
       154 + 26 = 180 so _____

Have a go

Try using a computer to write down some opposite subtraction and addition sums at home. Type them into a spreadsheet or document and print them out.

Teacher's tips

= means 'is the same as'. Start with the answer from the number sentence given, then take away the number that was added originally to get the number you started with.

7: Multiplication

While the children are playing outside in the garden, I have been putting the drinks on the table for snack time. How many are there altogether?

$$5 + 5 + 5 + 5 = 20$$
$$\text{or } 4 + 4 + 4 + 4 + 4 = 20$$
$$\text{or } 4 \times 5 = 20$$
$$\text{or } 5 \times 4 = 20$$

If you count things in groups, you are multiplying.

Get ready

Try these multiplication questions. Use the pictures above or draw dots to help you.

1   $4 \times 2 =$

2   $2 \times 5 =$

3   $2 \times 4 =$

4   $5 \times 3 =$

5   $3 \times 3 =$

6   $4 \times 3 =$

Let's practise

These words and phrases are used in multiplication.

| double | times | multiplied by | lots of | groups of |

Now try these questions.

7 4 lots of 5 ☐

8 6 multiplied by 4 ☐

9 3 multiplied by 7 ☐

10 2 groups of 8 ☐

11 4 times 0 ☐

12 5 times 5 ☐

13 Double 6 ☐

14 3 groups of 4 ☐

15 6 multiplied by 6 ☐

16 10 multiplied by 5 ☐

Have a go

It is always worth learning and practising your times tables or 'multiplication facts'. Knowing them off by heart makes Maths much easier. With the help of a grown-up, you could make a poster to display them on your wall. Once you have learnt them, you will be like an elephant – and never forget!

Teacher's tips

Multiplication can be done in any order, so change the question round to make it easier if it helps. For instance '5 lots of 7' might be harder than '7 lots of 5' – do it in the order that you find easiest.

8: Division

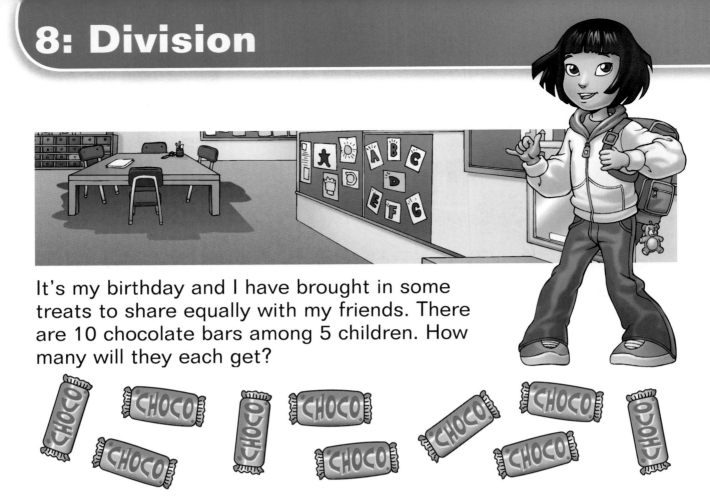

It's my birthday and I have brought in some treats to share equally with my friends. There are 10 chocolate bars among 5 children. How many will they each get?

That's right, they will get 2 bars each! We can write this as 10 ÷ 5 = 2.

Get ready

Share these sweets equally among the children.

1. Share 6 sweets between myself and Megan. _____ each

2. Share 6 sweets among Alfie, Jamelia and Kim. _____ each

3. Share 8 sweets between myself and Jamelia. _____ each

4. Share 9 sweets among Alfie, Kim and Megan. _____ each

5. Share 10 sweets between myself and Megan. _____ each

Let's practise

Here are words and phrases used in division.

share   halve   divide

divided by

equal groups of

left over

Now try these.

6 Share 16 between 2. _____

7 Divide 9 by 3. _____

8 Halve 12. _____

9 If I divide 5 by 2, how many are left over? _____

10 How many equal groups of 4 can I make from 8? _____

11 Divide £10 by 2. _____

12 How many piles of 5 cubes can you make from a pile of 20 cubes? _____

Have a go

At meal times, practise sharing out spoonfuls of food equally among your family.

Make sure everyone gets their fair share!

Teacher's tips

Draw a simple sketch of the question to help you work out the answer, or use some dry pasta/marbles/buttons to practise dividing sets of objects into equal groups.

9: Written addition

At Kids Club we have been practising adding, subtracting, multiplying and dividing, using a pencil and paper. Let me show you how to do addition.

This is a way of adding a two-digit number to another two-digit number.

You can break the numbers down so they are easier to add.

> **76 + 47** breaks down to **70 + 40 + 6 + 7**,
> which equals **110** and **13**,
> so the total is **123**.

 **Get ready**

Use a pencil and some spare paper to add these numbers. Break them down into tens and units.

The first one has been done for you.

1. 18 + 25 = (breaks down to **10 + 20 + 8 + 5**, which equals **30** and **13**, so the total is **43**).

2. 24 + 26 = _____

3. 21 + 39 = _____

4. 37 + 34 = _____

5. 39 + 28 = _____

Let's practise

Now try another writing method for adding two-digit numbers.

The sum is 57 + 45.
Write the numbers as shown here. Add the tens column first and then the units column. Then add the two totals for the answer.

(50 + 40)
(7 + 5)

(90 + 12)

$$\begin{array}{r} 57 \\ + \ 45 \\ \hline 90 \\ + \ 12 \\ \hline 102 \end{array}$$

Write these questions out vertically as shown above on a spare sheet of paper, then write the answers in the boxes below.

6 74 + 38 =

7 82 + 25 =

8 66 + 92 =

9 49 + 73 =

10 18 + 53 =

11 89 + 27 =

12 73 + 24 =

13 46 + 34 =

14 56 + 28 =

15 99 + 99 =

Have a go

Ask a grown-up how they were taught to add at school. Show them the two ways you have been practising. Teach them how to use these methods!

Teacher's tips

Break down numbers over 20 into 'tens' and 'units' by saying them aloud slowly and listening carefully to the two parts of the number. When you add the units together, if the answer is more than 10 remember to 'carry' (or add) the extra ten into the tens.

10: Written subtraction

This is a good way of doing subtraction using a pencil and paper. You can count up from the smaller number to the larger number in steps. Then you add up the steps to find the answer. Let me show you how.

$$74 - 46 = ?$$

$$46 + 4 = 50$$
$$50 + 20 = 70$$
$$70 + 4 = 74$$

$$4 + 20 + 4 = 28$$
so $$74 - 46 = 28$$

Get ready

Use Jamelia's pencil and paper method to work these out. Write the questions out on a spare piece of paper, then write the answers in the boxes below.

1. $24 - 15$ ☐

2. $46 - 29$ ☐

3. $52 - 37$ ☐

4. $73 - 25$ ☐

5. $68 - 19$ ☐

6. $85 - 46$ ☐

7. $77 - 52$ ☐

8. $82 - 38$ ☐

9. $56 - 19$ ☐

10. $91 - 65$ ☐

I have another method to show you. You take too much and then give some back!

74 − 46 = ?
74 − 50 = 24   *(Round up the 46 to the nearest 10, so you take away 50.)*
24 + 4 = **28**   *(50 is 4 more than 46, so this needs to be added back on.)*

Use this paper and pencil method to answer these questions. Write the questions out on a spare piece of paper and then write the answers in the boxes below.

11   73 − 39 [ ]

12   95 − 23 [ ]

13   52 − 35 [ ]

14   69 − 47 [ ]

15   83 − 19 [ ]

16   72 − 46 [ ]

17   92 − 29 [ ]

18   33 − 15 [ ]

19   87 − 38 [ ]

20   155 − 26 [ ]

 **Have a go**

Practise the two methods. Ask a grown-up how they do paper and pencil subtraction. Show them how you do yours. Which do you think is the easiest method to use?

Teacher's tips

Always write down your working out using these methods. When you're rounding up numbers to make subtraction easier, don't forget you must add the difference between the actual number and the 'rounded' number to your final answer.

I have been naughty again! I rubbed out some of the numbers in these calculations that we have to do for our homework. Can you help fill in the gaps before Charlie finds out?

Here is one example:

6 × ? = 12. The missing digit is 2 because 6 × 2 = 12.

 **Get ready**

This is the homework list.

1. 6 + ⬜ = 9

2. ⬜ + 7 = 14

3. 2 + 8 = ⬜

4. ⬜ + 6 = 6

5. 3 + ⬜ = 10

6. 6 − 2 = ⬜

7. 8 − ⬜ = 3

8. ⬜ − 4 = 8

9. 11 − ⬜ = 7

10. ⬜ − 2 = 3

Let's practise

Can you help me do the next list?

11   [   ] $+ 5 = 13$

12 $9 +$ [   ] $= 11$

13 $8 + 8 =$ [   ]

14 $12 -$ [   ] $= 7$

15   [   ] $- 9 = 1$

16   [   ] $- 4 = 4$

17 $7 -$ [   ] $= 0$

18   [   ] $\times 7 = 35$

19 $2 \times$ [   ] $= 8$

20 $6 \times 2 =$ [   ]

21   [   ] $\times 3 = 9$

22 $5 \times$ [   ] $= 25$

23   [   ] $\times 3 = 12$

24 $2 \times 8 =$ [   ]

Here are some division calculations.

25 $8 \div$ [   ] $= 4$

26   [   ] $\div 5 = 2$

27 $15 \div 5 =$ [   ]

28 $20 \div$ [   ] $= 2$

29   [   ] $\div 1 = 16$

30 $21 \div$ [   ] $= 7$

31   [   ] $\div 2 = 7$

32 $40 \div$ [   ] $= 4$

Have a go

Write down ten calculations on a large piece of paper, for example $4 \times 3 = 12$. Cover up one number in each calculation and ask a friend to work out the missing number. How many do they get right?

Teacher's tips

Look at the symbols in the number sentence very carefully to make sure you are doing the correct calculation. '=' means 'is the same as' so make sure both sides of the number sentence equal the same number.

12: Number sentences

We like to play Maths games at Kids Club. My favourite is turning Maths statements from words to number sentences. Let me show you how to play 'Change Words to Numbers'.

You have to use the five symbols, +, −, ×, ÷ and = .

The word statements are: A quad-bike has four wheels. Three quad-bikes have twelve wheels.

I am going to turn these into a number sentence. It's: $4 \times 3 = 12$. One point to me!

 **Get ready**

Turn these into number sentences using +, −, ×, ÷ and = .

1. A comic costs twenty pence and a drink costs ten pence. They cost thirty pence altogether. _____

2. A tricycle has three wheels. Three tricycles have nine wheels.

   _____

3. Twenty sweets shared equally between five friends is four sweets each. _____

4. Alfie has eight marbles but loses six. He has two marbles left.

   _____

Let's practise

Now try these. Remember to use the four operation symbols and the equals sign.

(5) I have twelve toy cars. Alfie gives me seven more. I now have nineteen toy cars. _____

(6) A pizza is cut into eight equal pieces. Four people have two slices each.

_____

(7) Seven children have five pencils each. There are thirty-five pencils altogether.

_____

(8) Sixteen candles are burning. Five go out. Eleven are left alight.

_____

(9) A horse has four legs. Six horses have twenty-four legs.

_____

(10) Write your own word problem for this number sentence: $36 \div 6 = 6$.

_____

_____

_____

Have a go

Challenge a grown-up to play 'Change Words to Numbers'. Take it in turns to write the word statements and the number sentences. The younger person goes first!

Teacher's tips

Underline the quantities and the action words to help you focus on the important parts of the story. Think about what the action words mean in maths language, and where the '=' should go in your number sentence.

How have I done?

Answer these questions to see how well you have done at Kids Club.

Each part of a question is worth one mark. The total number of marks is 28.

1   a) 4 + 5 = ☐   b) 2 + 8 = ☐

2   a) 34 + 6 = ☐   b) 27 + 7 = ☐

3   a) What is the sum of 12 and 9? _____

   b) How many is 11 plus 8? _____

4   What is the total of this shopping bill?

   ☐

Tea   60p
Milk   28p
Sugar 32p

5   a) 10 − 8 = ☐   b) 10 − 4 = ☐

6   a) 24 − 7 = ☐   b) 31 − 5 = ☐

7   a) What is the difference between 3 and 11? _____

   b) What is 12 take away 9? _____

   c) Subtract 30 from 50. _____

   d) What is 8 less than 15? _____

8   Write an opposite subtraction sum to these calculations.

   a) 7 + 3 = 10, so _____

   b) 32 + 7 = 39, so _____

9 a) 5 × 3 = ☐   b) 2 × 7 = ☐   c) 3 × 6 = ☐

10 a) What is 5 multiplied by 4? ☐

b) How many is 2 groups of 7? ☐

11 a) Share 9 among 3. _____

b) Divide 15 by 5. _____

12 Record two different written methods to complete these calculations:

a) 74 + 57 _____   b) 83 − 29 _____

_____   _____

_____   _____

_____   _____

13 Fill in the missing number. 8 × ☐ = 40

14 Write these statements as a number sentence. Megan has twelve marbles and Amina has thirteen marbles. There are twenty-five marbles altogether. _____

Total ____
28

Well done for working so hard.
Come back to Kids Club soon!

Answers

UNIT 1

1 a b c d e f g h i j k l m n o p q r s t u v
   w x y z
2 A B C D E F G H I J K L M N O P Q R
   S T U V W X Y Z
3 e
4 h
5 l
6 o
7 r
8 u
9 c
10 i
11 p
12 t
13 w
14 y
15 b
16 e
17 m
18 q
19 s
20 w
21 b
22 c
23 p
24 q
25 t
26 u
27 A E I O U

UNIT 2

1 mug
2 bat
3 log
4 pin
5 sun
6 mop
7 hat
8 fan
9 pan
10 leg
11 pot
12 bed
13 bun
14 a cat on a mat   cat   mat
15 a ted on a bed   ted   bed
16 a king with a ring   king   ring
17 a clock on a rock   clock   rock
18 a mug and a jug   mug   jug

UNIT 3

1 I can hop.
2 A cow moos.
3 Fish can swim.
4 Ice cream is cold.
5 The sun is yellow.
6 I can sing.
7 The sky is blue.
8 Hens lay eggs.
9 A cat likes milk.
10 I can ride a bike.
11 The grass is green.
12 A dog barks.
13 I can read a book.
14 You bang a drum.
15 You swim in the sea.
16 A bird sings.
17 A frog hops.
18 You eat a cake.
19 A snake hisses.
20 A bike has got two wheels.

UNIT 4

1–6 show sentences with circle round capital letters and full stops.
7 A frog can hop.
8 A fish can swim.
9 A kangaroo can jump.
10 A lion can run.
11 A bird can fly.
12 An ant can crawl.
13 A monkey has got long arms.
14 An elephant has got a trunk.

UNIT 5

1 chat   check   chip   chop
2 shed   shop   ship   shut
3 thin   thick   think   thump
4 shop
5 chick
6 bath
7 torch
8 chop
9 shed
10 brush
11 path
12 thief
13 fish
14 chips
15 throne
16 (open – accept any appropriate answers)
17 (open – accept any appropriate answers)

UNIT 6

1 Charlie
2 Abbie
3 Jamelia
4 Megan
5 Kim
6 Amina
7 Alfie
8 Sunday Monday Tuesday Wednesday Thursday Friday Saturday
9 Solomon Grundy
   Born on Monday.
   Christened on Tuesday.
   Married on Wednesday.
   Ill on Thursday.
   Worse on Friday.
   Died on Saturday.
   Buried on Sunday.
   That was the end of Solomon Grundy.

UNIT 7

1 duck
2 bat
3 dog
4 cat
5 fox
6 horse
7 hen
8 cow
9 bird
10 rat
11 fruit: banana, orange, pear, strawberries, cherries, grapes
    vegetables: onion, peas, broccoli, carrot, potato, cabbage

UNIT 8

1. sheep feet three sweet
2. hoop boot stool spoon
3. You sweep with a broom.
4. Look at the green apples in the tree.
5. I sat on a stool by the pool.
6. When the moon is out I go to sleep.
7. Can you see three bees?
8. I put my boot on my foot.
9. ee words: sweep   green   tree   sleep   see   three   bees
10. oo words: broom   look   stool   pool   moon   boot   foot

UNIT 9

1. bang
2. eat
3. read
4. climb
5. ride
6. sleep
7. I smell with my nose.
8. I hear with my ears.
9. I see with my eyes.
10. I talk with my mouth.
11. I feel with my hands.
12. I walk with my feet.
13. pencil
14. chair
15. cow
16. bird
17. clock
18. spider

UNIT 10

1. kite
2. mate
3. ripe
4. cape
5. hate
6. gape
7. robe
8. cute
9. note
10. tube
11. pine
12. made
13. tap
14. slide
15. mop
16. mat
17. pipe
18. cube
19. pin
20. tube
21. hat
22. shine
23. rat
24. cane

UNIT 11

1. Ben and Mia
2. Ben
3. Mia
4. Max
5. to the seaside
6. no
7. his sungalsses and his hat
8. her flip-flops and a mat
9. an ice cream
10. a lolly
11. throw it and kick it
12. laugh and shout
13. Max the dog
14. red
15. go to bed

UNIT 12

1. dogs
2. brown
3. bushy tails
4. a brush
5. 125 centimetres long
6. woods
7. dens
8. yes
9. night
10. small animals
11. vixen
12. cubs

HOW HAVE I DONE?

1. a e i o u
2. pot bun bed pin rat
3. A dog barks.
4. A tiger has got stripes.
5. bath chair shed
6. Alfie got wet on Sunday.
7. trousers coat kettle jeans
8. moon sheep
9. teacher
10. I can ride a bike.
    The sun will shine tomorrow.
11. the seaside
12. foxes

WRITING

UNIT 1

1 Water, cola, squash, lemonade
2 Streamers, balloons, party-poppers, flags
3 Musical chairs, statues, tag, treasure hunt
4 Crisps, fruit, sandwiches, cakes
5 Spoons, cups, forks, plates
6 Amina went to the party with Alfie, Kim, Jamelia and Megan.
7 Alfie danced to pop, rap, rock and hip-hop music.
8 Kim made lots of decorations such as banners, streamers, flags and posters.
9 Megan had to move lots of furniture like the chairs, tables, desks and bookcases.
10 To clean up afterwards Jamelia used brooms, cloths, dustpans and brushes.

UNIT 2

Dear Michelle,

On Friday afternoon after school we had a party. We were so *excited*, everyone was happy. When we *arrived* we had a drink and something to eat. Alfie was dancing for most of the time. He *fell* over, bumped his head and began to cry *loudly*! Just then a clown came over. He gave Alfie an *enormous* balloon. He stopped crying and we all laughed and cheered. Then a *wonderful* thing happened. The clown *gave* each of us a balloon! Mine was in the shape of a beautiful *pony*. I knew you would have liked one the same.

Write soon!

Megan

UNIT 3

Kids Club is an *exciting* after-school club for *children* aged 5 to 11.

It is run by Charlie and *Abbie*, who are always ready to *help* and are great fun to have around.

There are lots of things to do and *games* to play. You can catch up on *homework* or try some art activities. There are snacks and *drinks* to keep everyone refreshed.

Sometimes Kids Club organises *events* for the school like a disco or summer fete.

Everyone *enjoys* themselves while they are there. Come and join us!

UNIT 4

1 First, put Hammy carefully into the exercise ball.
2 Secondly, lift the lid off the cage.
3 Next, empty the old bedding and sawdust into a rubbish bag.
4 Wipe all the surfaces clean with a damp cloth.
5 Cover the bottom of the cage with fresh sawdust.
6 Place a handful of shredded paper bedding on top of the sawdust.
7 Replace the lid of the cage.
8 Put Hammy back in the cage.
9 Finally, feed Hammy some fresh food and replace the water bottle.

UNIT 5

No answers required.

UNIT 6

The words for the glossary should be listed in the following order.

1 activities – pastimes done for fun and relaxation
2 charge – a price asked for a service
3 favourites – preferred to all others of the same kind
4 gym – a gymnasium; a room built for games and exercise
5 healthy – in good health or leading to good health
6 popular – liked and admired by many people
7 relax – to become less tense; to unwind
8 special – better than usual

UNITS 7–12

No answers required.

HOW HAVE I DONE?

No answers required.

GRAMMAR AND PUNCTUATION
UNIT 1
1 Kids Club is a fun place to be.
2 I have made lots of friends.
3 There are lots of things to do.
4 I think the leaders are cool.
5 I try and stay out of trouble!
6–10 Any suitable answers

UNIT 2
1 I like listening to music.
2 It makes me feel good.
3 I also enjoy playing football.
4 It is fun to play with friends.
5 I played football on holiday in France.
6 We went to the beach. It was a sunny day. I played in the sand. Alfie buried my sandals. Nobody could find them. I had to go home barefoot.

UNIT 3
1 Would you like to play a game?
2 OK, let's play cricket.
3 Alfie has the cricket set.
4 Alfie, can we play with you?
5 Of course. Do you have another ball?
6 Where
7 How
8 When
9 Who
10 Why
11 Which
12 What

UNIT 4
1 Hey, leave my skipping rope alone!
2 Can I borrow it?
3 Hand it back right now!
4 Why can't I play too?
5 Of course you can, but it would be nice if you asked me first!
6 Which is your favourite ride at the fair?
7 I love the dodgems, they're brilliant!
8 I always go on the roundabout with Alfie.
9 We like all of the rides at the fair in Freston.
10 Megan and Kim bumped me so hard with their dodgem, I banged my nose on the steering wheel!

UNIT 5

1 I went to France, Spain and Portugal in a camper van.
2 For my birthday I got cards, cakes and presents.
3 My friend Leo can play the piano, guitar and violin.
4 My best friends are Megan, Amina, Kim and Alfie.
5 I love football, cricket, rugby and swimming.
6 Sparrows, eagles and hawks are birds.
7 Golf, tennis and hockey are sports.
8 Milk, squash and cola are drinks.
9 Jam, butter and toast are types of food.
10 Carrots, sprouts and parsnips are vegetables.

UNIT 6

1 a ruler, a pencil, an apple
2 a hat, a shirt, a sock
3 an egg, an orange, an onion
4 a car, an aeroplane, a bicycle
5 an insect, a snake, an octopus
6 We went to London to see the Queen at Buckingham Palace.
7 Mr Jones was the coach driver.
8 We went on Saturday with Charlie and Abbie.
9 Alfie got lost in Saint James's Park.
10 He was found by Mr Jones and Amina.

UNIT 7

1 hairy
2 terrible
3 matted
4 long
5 smelly

Adjectives – shaggy, surprised, angry, smart, drenched
Nouns – lady, stick, pond, clothes, mud

UNIT 8

1 climbs
2 drops
3 travels
4 gobbles
5 breaks
6 are
7 is
8 is
9 is
10 Are
11 is
12 is
13 are
14 is
15 is

UNIT 9

Sample answers:

1 First
2 Secondly
3 Then
4 Next
5 Finally
6 First; Afterwards
7 Then
8 After a while
9 Eventually
10 Finally

UNIT 10

1 go
2 clean
3 see
4 is
5 breaks

UNIT 11

1–5 Any suitable answers
6 noisily
7 dangerously
8 yesterday
9 carefully
10 there
11 cleverly

HOW HAVE I DONE?

1   The robots took over the city. (1 mark)
2   I went to see my friends at the playground. (1 mark)
3   The bus is very full. Do you think we will be able to get on? (2 marks)
4   A cat makes a good pet. Get out of this room right now! (2 marks)
5   I went to the shops and bought a hat, some make-up, funny trousers, juggling balls and a unicycle. (3 marks)
6   an orange an apple a banana an apricot a pineapple (5 marks)
7   The crocodile has a very scaly skin.
    Its teeth are long and sharp.
    Salt-water crocodiles can grow to huge sizes. (3 marks)
8   *Sample answers:*
    A horse galloped in the field.
    The car raced on the track. (2 marks)
9   *Sample answer:*
    It was raining heavily. Eventually it stopped and the sun came out. (1 mark)
10 *Sample answers:*
    I swam in the sea. I am running to school. I will jump over the hedge. (3 marks)
11 proudly quickly happily (3 marks)

Total marks available = 26

MATHS

UNIT 1
1 Check numbers are traced accurately. Check each word is joined to the correct number.
2 Check the words are traced accurately
3 twelve, sixteen, seventeen, fifteen, fourteen

UNIT 2
1 13
2 14
3 12
4 11
5 15
6 10

7 8, 10, 11
8 12, 14, 15
9 14, 12, 10
10 13, 10, 9
11 16

UNIT 3
1 10, 20, 30, 40, 50, 60, 70, 80, 90, 100
2 28
3 45
4 32

5 36
6 57
7 64
8 a bird

UNIT 4
1 $4 + 3 = 7$
2 $2 + 3 = 5$
3 $5 + 6 = 11$
4 $5 + 4 = 9$
5 $6 + 4 = 10$
6 $4 + 4 = 8$
7 $4 + 2 = 6$

8 $5 + 3 = 8$
9 $3 + 4 = 7$
10 $4 + 4 = 8$
11 $7 + 1, 6 + 2, 5 + 3, 4 + 4$
   $7 + 0, 6 + 1, 4 + 3$
   $6 + 0, 5 + 1, 4 + 2$

UNIT 5
1 5 $9 - 4, 8 - 3, 10 - 5$
   3   $9 - 6, 4 - 1, 6 - 3, 8 - 5$
2 6
3 5
4 4
5 3
6 7
7 8
8 5
9 4

10 3
11 2
12 6
13 7
14 3
15 4
16 5
17 3

UNIT 6
1 2 wheels, 6 wheels
2 5 fingers, 10 fingers
3 3 legs, 12 legs
4 6 eggs, 12 eggs
5 5, 10

6 4, 12
7 4, 16
8 6, 24
9 8, 8
10 15, 15

UNIT 7
1 4
2 2
3 4
4 5
5 6 groups

6 5 groups
7 4, 4
8 4, 4
9 3, 3
10 8, 8

UNIT 8

1

accept any one part of two shaded

2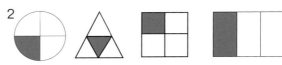

accept any one part of four shaded

3 3

4 5

5 2

6 3

7 Check 3 of the 4 parts are shaded on each shape.

UNIT 9

Check the correct shapes have been drawn.

1 cylinder

2 cone

3 sphere

4 cylinder

5 cube

6 cone

7 cube

8 sphere

9 Check the triangles have been shaded.

UNIT 10

1 3, 4, 6, 8, 9

2 4, 7, 10, 11, 19

3 12, 14, 15, 17, 20

4 6, 10, 13, 15, 18

5

6 1p, 2p, 5p, 10p, 20p

7 5p, 10p, 20p, 50p, £1

UNIT 11

1 half past eight

2 half past five

3 four o'clock

4 nine o'clock

5 half past seven

6 one o'clock

7 seven o'clock

8 half past eleven

9 Monday, Tuesday, Wednesday, Thursday, Friday, Saturday

10 1 → 4 → 3 → 2

11 4 → 3 → 2 → 1

12 4 → 1 → 3 → 2

UNIT 12

1 2 metres

2 4 metres

3 1 metre

4 3 metres

5 5 metres

6 spoon, cup, teapot, saucepan, bucket

7 right

8 left

9 left

10 right

HOW HAVE I DONE?

1 a) fifteen
   b) twenty

2 16

3 13

4 10, 20, 30, 40, 50, 60, 70, 80, 90, 100

5 47

6 5 + 3 = 8

7 12

8 7

9 9 − 5

10 3, 9

11 4

12 7, 7

13

accept any one part of four shaded

14 4

15 triangle

16

17 7, 10, 12, 17, 20

18 ten o'clock

19

20

SOLVING PROBLEMS
UNIT 1

1 4	4 4	7 6	10 4	13 6
2 10	5 10	8 16	11 7	14 11
3 3	6 14	9 12	12 2	

Have a go
Jamelia (in 10 seconds)

UNIT 2

1 5	3 6	5 8	7 3	9 7	11 10
2 7	4 6	6 5	8 10	10 7	12 21

UNIT 3

1 8	4 9	7 4	10 7
2 5	5 5	8 2	11 14
3 7	6 2	9 2	

UNIT 4

1 9	3 12	5 10	7 18	9 18
2 8	4 4	6 25	8 4	10 28

Have a go
30

UNIT 5

1 3	4 5	7 6	10 4	13 30
2 2	5 4	8 5	11 5	14 7
3 2	6 6	9 6	12 10	15 24

UNIT 6

1 Capacity of shell – millilitres
2 Width of pine cone – centimetres
3 Weight of nest – grams
4 Capacity of pond – litres
5 Length of tree – metres
6 a) g   b) g   c) kg
7 a) cm   b) m   c) cm
8 a) ml   b) l   c) ml

UNIT 7

1 5m	6 28	11 40kg
2 10m	7 45cm	12 8
3 14	8 15kg	13 5cm
4 19	9 5	14 12l
5 20	10 75cm	

UNIT 8

1 12cm
2 25cm
3 75g
4 500ml
5 a) 12cm   b) 8cm
6 Answers will vary.
7 Answers will vary.

UNIT 9

1 28p	**3** 46p	**5** £24	**7** 25p	**9** £2
2 65p	**4** 38p	**6** 28p	**8** 5p	**10** £1.08

Have a go
Accept any correct answers.

UNIT 10

1 15, 16, 17	**6** 23, 25, 27	**11** 35, 30, 25
2 31, 32, 33	**7** 42, 45, 48	**12** 55, 65, 75
3 50, 51, 52	**8** 56, 59, 62	**13** 63, 57, 51
4 40, 50, 60	**9** 76, 81, 86	**14** 33, 42, 51
5 28, 30, 32	**10** 86, 82, 78	

UNIT 11

1 3 hours
2 1.00pm
3 Clock showing 9 o'clock
4 Clock showing 6 o'clock
5 Clock showing 2 o'clock
6 4.00pm
7 15 minutes
8 30 minutes
9 60 minutes
10 Sample answer: between 5.00pm and 5.15pm

UNIT 12

1 a) 3 b) 6
2 5
3 Sample answer: 23 and 20
4 Answers will vary e.g. 14 + 1 or 10 + 5
5 18
6 36
7 1, 1, 17; 1, 3, 15; 1, 5, 13; 1, 7, 11; 1, 9, 9; 3, 3, 13; 3, 5, 11; 3, 7, 9; 5, 5, 9; 5, 7, 7. There are 6 combinations of each of these groups, giving a total of 60 possibilities.
8 Answers will vary e.g. 23 + 2 or 19 + 6
9 Sample answer: 2 × 20p, 1 × 10p, 1 × 5p
10 Left to right from the top: blue square, white square, pink square, red square, yellow triangle, grey triangle

HOW HAVE I DONE?

1 22	**9** 4	**17** £6
2 9	**10** 5	**18** 10p
3 14	**11** Scales	**19** 14, 11
4 25	**12** cm	**20** 33, 37
5 6	**13** 4	**21** Clock showing 8 o'clock
6 2	**14** 24	**22** 6.30am
7 32	**15** 800ml	**23** 8
8 30	**16** 7cm	**24** Weigh the same.

MENTAL MATHS

UNIT 1
1 10 4 15 7 Alfie 10 28 13 Alfie 16 52
2 8 5 20 8 24 11 30 14 Jamelia
3 11 6 Kim 9 27 12 22 15 54

UNIT 2
1 9 7 3 13 23 18 8
2 9 8 3 14 22
3 14 9 47 15 Sample answer:
4 20 10 90 $10 + 4 = 14$
5 18 11 27 16 2
6 23 12 27 17 30

UNIT 3
1 30p 3 28p 5 33p 7 92p 9 78p 11 Megan 13 £2.44
2 28p 4 21p 6 82p 8 74p 10 71p 12 £1.53

UNIT 4
1 8 5 7 9 4 13 16 17 31 21 50
2 5 6 2 10 3 14 9 18 47 22 Jamelia
3 0 7 6 11 Jamelia 15 23 19 30
4 10 8 9 12 12 16 20 20 69

UNIT 5
1 3 5 3 9 3 13 60 17 6
2 4 6 4 10 11 14 6 18 9
3 6 7 2 11 30 15 14 19 19
4 1 8 10 12 18 16 6 20 10

UNIT 6
1 $9 - 5 = 4$ 6 $30 - 3 = 27$ 11 $45 - 7 = 38$
2 $10 - 7 = 3$ 7 $23 - 1 = 22$ 12 $74 - 20 = 54$
3 $14 - 6 = 8$ 8 $33 - 5 = 28$ 13 $37 - 9 = 28$
4 $15 - 5 = 10$ 9 $52 - 10 = 42$ 14 $180 - 26 = 154$
5 $14 - 2 = 12$ 10 $70 - 8 = 62$

UNIT 7
1 8 5 9 9 21 13 12
2 10 6 12 10 16 14 12
3 8 7 20 11 0 15 36
4 15 8 24 12 25 16 50

UNIT 8
1 3 3 4 5 5 7 3 9 1 11 £5
2 2 4 3 6 8 8 6 10 2 12 4

UNIT 9
2 $20 + 20 + 4 + 6 = 40 + 10 = 50$ 4 $30 + 30 + 7 + 4 = 60 + 11 = 71$
3 $20 + 30 + 1 + 9 = 50 + 10 = 60$ 5 $30 + 20 + 9 + 8 = 50 + 17 = 67$

	6	7	8	9	10	11
	74	82	66	49	18	89
	+ 38	+ 25	+ 92	+ 73	+ 53	+ 27
	100	100	150	110	60	100
	12	7	8	12	11	16
	112	107	158	122	71	116

12	73	13	46	14	56	15	99
	+ 24		+ 34		+ 28		+ 99
	90		70		70		180
	7		10		14		18
	97		80		84		198

UNIT 10

1 $24 - 15 = 5 + 4 = 9$ 2 $46 - 29 = 1 + 10 + 6 = 17$
3 $52 - 37 = 3 + 10 + 2 = 15$ 4 $73 - 25 = 5 + 40 + 3 = 48$
5 $68 - 19 = 1 + 40 + 8 = 49$ 6 $85 - 46 = 4 + 30 + 5 = 39$
7 $77 - 52 = 8 + 10 + 7 = 25$ 8 $82 - 38 = 2 + 40 + 2 = 44$
9 $56 - 19 = 1 + 30 + 6 = 37$ 10 $91 - 65 = 5 + 20 + 1 = 26$
11 $73 - 39 = 73 - 40 + 1 = 33 + 1 = 34$ 16 $72 - 46 = 72 - 50 + 4 = 22 + 4 = 26$
12 $95 - 23 = 95 - 30 + 7 = 65 + 7 = 72$ 17 $92 - 29 = 92 - 30 + 1 = 62 + 1 = 63$
13 $52 - 35 = 52 - 40 + 5 = 12 + 5 = 17$ 18 $33 - 15 = 33 - 20 + 5 = 13 + 5 = 18$
14 $69 - 47 = 69 - 50 + 3 = 19 + 3 = 22$ 19 $87 - 38 = 87 - 40 + 2 = 47 + 2 = 49$
15 $83 - 19 = 83 - 20 + 1 = 63 + 1 = 64$ 20 $155 - 26 = 155 - 30 + 4 = 125 + 4 = 129$

UNIT 11

1 3	7 5	13 16	19 4	25 2	31 14
2 7	8 12	14 5	20 12	26 10	32 10
3 10	9 4	15 10	21 3	27 3	
4 0	10 5	16 8	22 5	28 10	
5 7	11 8	17 7	23 4	29 16	
6 4	12 2	18 5	24 16	30 3	

UNIT 12

1 $20p + 10p = 30p$ 4 $8 - 6 = 2$ 7 $7 \times 5 = 35$ 10 Answers will vary.
2 $3 \times 3 = 9$ 5 $12 + 7 = 19$ 8 $16 - 5 = 11$
3 $20 \div 5 = 4$ 6 $8 \div 4 = 2$ 9 $4 \times 6 = 24$

HOW HAVE I DONE?

1 a) 9 b) 10
2 a) 40 b) 34
3 a) 21 b) 19
4 £1.20
5 a) 2 b) 6
6 a) 17 b) 26

7 a) 8 b) 3 c) 20 d) 7
8 a) $10 - 3 = 7$ b) $39 - 7 = 32$
9 a) 15 b) 14 c) 18
10 a) 20 b) 14
11 a) 3 b) 3

12 a) $74 + 57 = 70 + 50 + 4 + 7 = 120 + 11 = 131$

	74
+	57
	120
	11
	131

b) $83 - 29 = 1 + 50 + 3 = 54$; $83 - 29 = 83 - 30 + 1 = 53 + 1 = 54$
13 5
14 $12 + 13 = 25$